R. SCOTT STEVENSON

FAMOUS ILLNESSES IN HISTORY

1962

EYRE & SPOTTISWOODE

LONDON

First published 1962
Reprinted 1963
© *1962 R. Scott Stevenson*
Printed in Great Britain by
Cox & Wyman Ltd
London, Fakenham and Reading
Catalogue No. 6/2472/1

CONTENTS

CONTENTS

DRAWINGS IN TEXT

INTRODUCTION

WE are apt to be a little complacent about the triumphs of medicine and surgery in our time. The span of life has increased by fifteen years in the past fifty, giving us new problems with an increasingly ageing population. The old plagues have disappeared, hospitals for infectious diseases are empty, and even in the tropics malaria, yellow fever and sleeping sickness have on the whole been vanquished. One should remember, however, that Sir John Erichsen in 1873 and Lord Moynihan in 1932 each in his day prophesied that operative surgery had no more frontiers to conquer – Erichsen, just before Lister had transformed the old Hunterian surgery into the new, and Moynihan, when the surgery of the brain was in its infancy and the surgery of the heart and the lung had not yet been born. And no surgeon can remain complacent while the five-year survival rate in operations for cancer of the stomach is only 5 per cent and in cancer of the lung about 20 per cent.

The advances, nevertheless, during the past fifty years, both in diagnostic methods and in treatment, in the whole conception of great fields of medicine, have been revolutionary. Not only the more spectacular antibiotics and chemotherapy, insulin and liver therapy, the vitamins, cortisone and the synthetic steroids, pituitrin and the other hormones, allergy and the antihistamines, new techniques in pathology and virology (with the aid of the electron-microscope), advances in biochemistry, the anaemias and blood transfusion, X-rays and radiotherapy, radio-isotopes, cardiology and electrocardiography, the bronchoscope, gastroscope and cysto-scope; but also the new exploration of the mind and advances in neurology and psychiatry, with modern psychotherapy and the new sedative and tranquillizing drugs.

Abdominal surgery has made enormous strides since in 1902 King Edward VII's surgeons 'feared the result of so delicate and infrequent an operation' as removal of the appendix. The two World Wars have been given the credit of the development of orthopaedic surgery, blood transfusion, and plastic surgery; but War does not of itself produce advances in medicine or surgery – it only increases, because of its urgency, the tempo of the advances.

Delicate new techniques have been introduced into ophthalmic and otological surgery (in which the operating microscope has surprisingly become the otologist's chief weapon), and new methods of anaesthesia have rendered feasible marked technical advances in surgery, especially in cranial and thoracic surgery. Advances have been widespread in paediatrics, child health and child welfare, in the treatment and rehabilitation of the blind and the deaf, in public health and in dietetics, in physiotherapy and rehabilitation in general, and in higher standards of education and training alike for doctors, nurses, auxiliaries, technicians, and hospital administrators. New drugs, however, have produced new problems in sensitivity, in unsuspected infections, and in side-effects.

The still mysterious problem of cancer will undoubtedly be solved some day, sooner or later, slow as is the progress of cancer research. There is much that remains unknown today about the functions of the body and its behaviour in health and disease; but in spite of new inventions and dazzling equipment, research laboratories and operating theatres, the trained and experienced brain of the doctor is still the best diagnostic instrument.

II

It has been said that the patient is the 'forgotten man', the 'unsung hero' in medicine, but this is not quite true, and in the following chapters the patient usually emerges with more credit than his doctors. Medical history has recorded, among others, that the name of Pasteur's patient (with rabies) was Joseph Meister, and William Beaumont's (with a gastric fistula) Alexis St. Martin. Diseases are, however, still called after the physician who first described them (Kinnier Wilson and Sheehan recently, as well as Bright and Addison long ago), though the anatomists now prefer to use polysyllablic and obscure descriptions instead of the former succinct and familiar eponyms.

Osler wrote, in his book of essays *Aequanimitas*: 'the philosophies of one age have become the absurdities of the next, and the foolishness of yesterday has become the wisdom of tomorrow.' The seventeenth century produced not only the Royal Society in 1663, but the learned William Harvey (who died in 1657), the discoverer of the circulation of the blood, and the wise Thomas Sydenham (who died in 1689), the greatest physician of the age, who described fevers accurately, and prescribed iron for anaemia, chichona bark (containing quinine) for ague or malaria, and laudanum (opium with cloves and cinnamon) to relieve pain. Nevertheless, towards the end of that comparatively enlightened century we are still shocked to read the dreadful description of the last illness of King Charles II, with fourteen physicians around him, using some disgusting and some magical remedies, forcing prescription after prescription upon him, blistering his shaved head, purging him and making him vomit. King George V in 1928 was treated more kindly and logically, but still by twelve physicians and surgeons; and Franklin (not yet President) Roosevelt's doctor, a year or two before, had called into consultation a once-distinguished but outdated veteran surgeon, who made the wrong diagnosis and prescribed the wrong treatment.

In medicine and surgery, a correct diagnosis must always precede treatment, and it was his study of the diagnostic methods of Dr Joseph Bell of Edinburgh that led Conan Doyle to create the character of Sherlock Holmes. In this book I have tried to emphasize interesting problems of diagnosis in illnesses that may have influenced the course of history, including some post-mortem examinations because the importance of a post-mortem is in checking (and not infrequently correcting) the diagnosis.

I knew personally a number of the physicians and surgeons involved in the more recent cases, and the book first began to take shape in my mind when Sir Frederick Hewitt, the anaesthetist, told me that at the famous operation on the appendix of King Edward VII the appendix was not removed, as I and most other people had believed. I knew most of the medical attendants in the case of King George V, especially Mr Wilfred Trotter, the surgeon. I had a personal contact even in the case of the Emperor Napoleon III, for my friend Dr Paul Dubs of Paris was able to introduce me to the grandson of Dr Henri Conneau, the Emperor's physician and close friend, who had treasured some interesting unpublished documents concerning his grandfather. I had several talks with Mr Mark Hovell, Sir Morell Mackenzie's assistant in the treatment of the Emperor Frederick III, as well as with others of Mackenzie's friends, and I had the privilege of examining the telegrams in the Royal Archives at Windsor from Mackenzie to Sir James Reid, Queen Victoria's physician.

The case of the Emperor Frederick appears to be of continuing interest, for I was invited to lecture on it at Yale in 1957 and to read a paper on Morell Mackenzie at the Royal Society of Medicine last May. Some twenty years ago I wrote a short biography of Morell Mackenzie, which was published in 1946 by Messrs Heinemann (Medical Books) Ltd and has long been out of print. It was, however, about the physician rather than about his patient, for I hoped then to help to rehabilitate the professional reputation of Morell Mackenzie. But the denigration of Mackenzie continues, and in 1960 there was published on both sides of the Atlantic *The Triumph of Surgery*, translated from the German of Herr Jürgen Thorwald, which discussed the treatment of the Emperor Frederick. The author, being German, accepted as gospel the German side of the controversy, repeating all the old biased opinions and vindictive stories. I thought, therefore, that I should examine anew and in more detail than I had done previously, all the books and documents on the subject to which I had access, to see whether I had told the truth or had been misled. My conclusions are given here, in Chapter V.

III

Many of the happiest hours of my life have been spent in libraries, and I am indebted to two in particular, without the help of which this book could never have been written, the Library of the Royal Society of Medicine, London, and the Garrison Library, Gibraltar. The former is the leading medical library of Europe, with 400,000 books and over 2,000 current medical periodicals; to Mr Philip Wade, the librarian, and Miss Muriel Evans, deputy librarian, I owe grateful thanks for generous help in London and for sending photostats, reprints and other essential material to me at Gibraltar. The Garrison Library, Gibraltar, founded in 1793 and built at the instance of William Pitt in 1804, has many unexpected treasures, especially rare books of the early nineteenth century and files of *The Times* and *Illustrated London News* since 1850; again I should like sincerely to thank Mr E. F. E. Ryan, the secretary, and Miss L. M. Lavagna, the senior librarian, for constant assistance.

My old friend, Mr T. J. Shields, until recently librarian to the British Medical Association, was particularly helpful in the early stages of this book, as were Miss E. Stiff, librarian at the Athenaeum Club, and Mr R. J. Durling, assistant librarian at the Wellcome Historical Medical Library. Mademoiselle Paule Dumaître, conservateur at the Bibliothèque of the Faculté de Médecine, Paris, not only helped me in her own library, but gave me useful introductions at the Bibliothèque Nationale and the Archives Nationales. My colleagues at the Colonial Hospital, Gibraltar, Mr D. J. Toomey, Mr J. M. Hastings, Dr J. J. Giraldi and Dr C. M. Montegriffo, have checked medical statements that were a little off my own beat. To all of them I should like to express my gratitude.

I have to acknowledge also the kindness of the Editors of the

British Medical Journal, The Lancet, and *The Times,* for allowing me to quote from their columns, and of the numerous authors and publishers, whose names are given in my lists of references, for similarly allowing me to quote from their books. Some of my facts come from unpublished material, and some from what the *Dictionary of National Biography* calls 'private information; personal knowledge'.

Gibraltar, 1962.   R. S. S.

CHAPTER I

TEAMWORK AND THE RECOVERY OF KING GEORGE V

KING GEORGE V's long illness in 1928–29, and his slow recovery, gained him the sincere sympathy of his people; and his Silver Jubilee celebrations six years later, in 1935, were spontaneous and enthusiastic. It had not always been so. As Sir Harold Nicolson wrote in his *King George V*: 'The ordinary citizens learnt to regard King George both as the father of his people and as the reflection and magnification of their own collective virtues. Dutifully he subordinated his own preferences and prejudices, his many unconcealed likes and dislikes, to an excellent perception of his historical function. Under his guidance, the British Monarchy emerged from a period of international convulsion, from a period at home of slow silent revolution, with enhanced influence and repute.'

King George V was the younger son of King Edward VII, and became heir apparent on the death of his more dashing but less stable brother, the Duke of Clarence, in January 1893. He had spent his life (including his boyhood, for he was a cadet in the old *Britannia*) in the Royal Navy, had developed a 'quarter-deck' manner that was not universally popular, and had a quick temper. He married his elder brother's fiancée, the Princess Mary of Teck, who had been carefully picked and trained for the position under the far-seeing eye of Queen Victoria, and to whom he became genuinely devoted. But he was not very successful in the harshly disciplined upbringing of his sons.

He succeeded his father in 1910, and found himself at once involved with difficult political problems – the Liberal Government's struggle with the House of Lords, National Insurance, women's suffrage, successive general elections, Ulster and the Irish controversies, the growing menace of Germany and eventually the war of 1914–18. Then came the Russian Revolution, Sinn Fein and the Irish Rebellion, the first Labour Government in 1924, and the General Strike of 1926. In all these difficulties the King acted as a conscientious and peace-loving constitutional sovereign, and enhanced his reputation at home and abroad. Indeed the present-day adulation of the monarchy can be said to stem directly from the solid virtues of King George V and Queen Mary, and from the high regard of their subjects, which was in part brought about by the mass appeal of the new invention, broadcasting.

II

King George V was an inveterate diarist, and in his diary for November 21st, 1928, he wrote: 'Feverish cold they call it, and I retired to bed'. He had been at Balmoral in the autumn, had had a short visit to Sandringham, and had returned to Buckingham Palace on November 19th. It was to be ten months before he resumed his normal activities.

Lord Dawson of Penn of the London Hospital, ennobled after the 'Dawson Report' of 1920 which foreshadowed the National Health Service, consulting physician to the Army in the 1914–18 War, the most popular consultant physician of the day and Physician to H.M. the King, joined Sir Stanley Hewett, Physician-in-Ordinary, in consultation in the evening of November 21st; they were unable to detect any localized signs and formed a provisional diagnosis of a blood infection. A blood culture made next day by Dr Lionel Whitby (afterwards Regius Professor at Cambridge University and a leading authority on the blood) yielded a growth of streptococcus. Early on 23rd November the same streptococcus appeared in small clots of blood that were coughed up. Sisters

Purdie, Black, Davies and Gordon, from the Westminster, the London, and St. Thomas's Hospitals, were engaged to nurse the King – representatives of the nursing profession from England, Scotland, Wales and Ireland.

On November 22nd, 1928, an official bulletin was issued, signed by Sir Stanley Hewett and Lord Dawson of Penn, which stated that 'There is some congestion of one lung'. X-ray examination of the King by a portable apparatus was carried out on November 23rd by Dr H. Graham Hodgson, then diagnostic radiologist to King's College Hospital, an excellent technician and a tall, good-looking man, who owed much to Lord Dawson's patronage.

On 25th November, the bulletin read: 'The King has had a disturbed day due to an increase in the fever.' On 26th November, the bulletin read: 'The temperature is now 101.6°, but the pleurisy has not extended further, and the strength is maintained.'

On 30th November, the bulletin, 'Some improvement', was signed by Sir Humphry Rolleston as well as by Sir Stanley Hewett and Lord Dawson of Penn. Sir Humphry Rolleston was called in, it was explained, 'to have an independent opinion in the general review of the case'. But Sir Humphry, Regius Professor of Physic at Cambridge University, and the last of the scholar-physicians, was never very helpful in consultation, for with his wide-ranging knowledge of medical literature he always remembered so many possible alternatives.

On 4th December a Council of State was appointed to deal with public business, comprising the Queen, the Prince of Wales, the Duke of York, the Archbishop of Canterbury, the Lord Chancellor and the Prime Minister. The Prince of Wales and the Duke of Gloucester were in Tanganyika, and Prince George in the West Indies, but the Duke and Duchess of York were in London.

In the early hours (12.10 a.m.) of 3rd December a bulletin was issued: 'In spite of the improvement in the lung, anxiety concerning the strength of the heart persists.' This was signed by Sir Stanley Hewett, Lord Dawson of Penn, Sir E. Farquhar Buzzard (Regius

Professor of Medicine at Oxford University and a good neurologist and administrator, not a chest physician) and Dr Lionel E. H. Whitby, who had been called previously to make a bacteriological examination. A later bulletin on 3rd December read: 'Temperature 99·8°, and there is a slight improvement in the general condition.'

The afternoon of 4th December brought together for the first time all the five doctors who had been in attendance during the course of the King's illness, for a general consultation. On 5th December the bulletin read: 'The recrudescence of infection is still active. The strength is maintained', and on 6th December: 'The general condition is slowly improving and the infective process, which remains severe, is becoming more localized.'

The *British Medical Journal* published on Friday, 7th December, stated: 'As early as practicable in the illness a blood culture was taken and a positive result obtained. The infection was coccal in character. Blood counts have shown a leucocytosis of the polymorphonuclear variety. Radiology has been useful, and the clear pictures obtained confirmed the clinical evidence that the lower two-thirds of the right lung was the area involved ... Therapy directed against the infection has taken the form of chemical antidotes, the raising of immunity, and the promotion of leucocytosis.'

An official statement issued on 9th December read: 'During the week there was great anxiety due to the fact that the infection involved the whole of the system. Now the physicians are dealing with a localized infection ... Both the needle exploration and the X-ray examination carried out on Friday (7th December) show there is no appreciable pleural effusion, and therefore there is no object in any operation.' On 10th December the bulletin read: 'The fever persists, due to some return of the general infection.'

On 11th December the Prince of Wales arrived back in London and drove straight from Victoria Station to Buckingham Palace. According to *The Times*, the King, though unaware of the Prince's expected arrival, immediately recognized and greeted him. Sir Harold Nicolson writes, however, 'He found his father barely conscious.'

A bulletin in the afternoon of 12th December stated: 'Some purulent fluid round the base of the right lung was removed by puncture this morning, and further drainage will be necessary.' Sir Harold Nicolson is more dramatic: 'On the afternoon of December 12th,' he writes [in his 'Life' of King George V], 'the twenty-second day of the illness, Lord Dawson, gazing at the unconscious figure on the bed, determined to make one more attempt to find the fatal fluid. Within a few seconds he had located the exact place. That evening an operation was performed.'

The Times for Thursday, 13th December 1928, stated that the following bulletin was issued by the King's doctors from Buckingham Palace last night: '8.45 p.m. – An operation on the King for the drainage of the right side of the chest has been successfully performed this evening. The condition of His Majesty is satisfactory.' (Signed) Stanley Hewett, Hugh M. Rigby (the surgeon), Francis Shipway (the anaesthetist), E. Farquhar Buzzard, Humphry Rolleston, Dawson of Penn. Sir Hugh Rigby, who performed the operation, was Surgeon-in-Ordinary to H.M. the King and, like Lord Dawson, on the staff of the London Hospital.

III

At the request of the editors of *The Lancet* and the *British Medical Journal* a statement was authorized for publication in the medical press on 14th December 1928: 'To make clear the nature of this long and exhausting illness, it is necessary to state that a general blood infection and toxaemia were in the first two weeks prominent features and caused at one time grave anxiety. Moreover, the case has not presented the characteristics of a typical pleuro-pneumonia. Seven days ago the evidences of general infection had become less prominent and the blood cultures were sterile, though all medical men will know that sterility of blood cultures is not conclusive evidence that general infection has ceased.

'During the last five days the temperature has again risen to a higher level, yet the pneumonic and pleural signs became at the

B

same time less marked, and neither pleural puncture nor study of new and excellent radiograms disclosed any appreciable effusion. Seeing, however, that the original pleurisy had involved the diaphragm, a careful watch has been kept for the formation of fluid between the lung and the diaphragm and its extension to the posterior pulmonary surface. This morning there were signs of this development accompanied by an increased leucocytosis. By exploratory puncture at the extreme right posterior base purulent fluid was obtained, which contains organisms morphologically resembling those previously found in the blood stream. Drainage will now be performed. Though this pleural localization of the infection, so anxiously anticipated and looked for, makes the direction of advance more defined and hopeful, there is still in prospect a long and difficult struggle.'

The bulletin issued from Buckingham Palace on the evening of 13th December stated: 'Though the King is still suffering from exhaustion, there is a slight improvement in His Majesty's condition this evening. The local condition remains satisfactory.'

Dr R. S. Woods, physician-in-charge of the department of physical medicine and electrology at the London Hospital, and Dr Frank D. Howitt, physician-in-charge of the physiotherapy and massage departments of the Prince of Wales's General Hospital, Tottenham, were called into consultation on Saturday afternoon, 15th December. The bulletin issued on Saturday evening stated: 'It has now been decided to employ ray therapy as part of the treatment,' which was in fact begun that afternoon.

According to *The Times* for 15th December 1928, the Queen replied to a message from Mr Coolidge, President of the United States: 'Though the recent operation successfully treated one phase of the King's serious illness, the consequences of the general infection will entail many weeks of slow and anxious progress before convalescence can be reached.' By the end of January 1929, over 100 bulletins had been issued. *The Lancet* for 29th December stated: 'Convalescence is now in sight', and on 9th February 1929, the

King was taken in an ambulance to Craigweil House, near Bognor; on 12th February he was allowed his first cigarette.

IV

On 27th March, Dr Cosmo Lang, the new Archbishop of Canterbury, went down to Bognor to do homage, and suggested that the King should address a message to his people giving thanks for his recovery. Lord Dawson, however, thought that this would be premature. On 15th May 1929, the King was at last strong enough to leave Bognor for Windsor. By the middle of June it was decided to hold a public Thanksgiving Service in Westminster Abbey, to which the King and Queen drove in state. But the wound in the King's side was still unhealed, for a local abscess had formed at the site of the operation. The King remarked to Lord Dawson: 'Fancy a Thanksgiving Service with an open wound in your back!' It is said (by Sir Harold Nicolson) that the immediate cause of the King's relapse a few days later was a visit from Mr J. H. Thomas, the Labour Cabinet Minister, whose ribald jokes always appealed to His Majesty. The King laughed so hilariously at one of them that the wound broke down and he suffered a relapse.

The usual causes of a persistent sinus in such a case are delay in the treatment of the empyema and inadequate drainage. Mr John Gore writes in his *Personal Memoir*: 'It became plain to the King's medical advisers, included among whom was the late Mr Wilfred Trotter, that for its cure [the abscess] it would be necessary to make an opening immediately over its site.'

At 11.40 a.m. on July 15th, the following bulletin was issued from Buckingham Palace: 'The operation on His Majesty the King has been performed. Portions of two ribs were removed, in order that the circumscribed abscess, $1\frac{1}{2}$ inches across, should be directly drained and treated. The condition of His Majesty is satisfactory.' This was signed by Sir Stanley Hewett, Sir Hugh M. Rigby, Mr Wilfred Trotter, Dr Francis E. Shipway, and Lord Dawson of Penn.

The operation was carried out in the King's bedroom. In addition to the five doctors by whom the bulletin is signed, there were also present in the Palace Mr Henry Martyn (Surgeon-Apothecary to H.M. Household at Windsor), who had spent the night there, and Dr H. Graham Hodgson, the radiologist, who took further X-ray photographs of the King's right chest in the past week. Next day the following bulletin was issued: 'His Majesty the King has passed a good night. Both the general and local conditions are satisfactory.'

The *British Medical Journal* for 20th July, 1929 contained the following note: 'At a consultation on 9th July between Lord Dawson, Sir Stanley Hewett, Sir Hugh Rigby, Mr Wilfred Trotter, and Mr H. L. Martyn, it was decided that a further operation on the King was necessary in order to provide adequate drainage for the residual abscess at the site of the empyema wound. This abscess communicated with the surface by an oblique sinus, which had become increasingly difficult to keep open. The size of the abscess (1½ inches across) and its position were determined by stereoscopic X-ray examination following injection of lipiodol through the sinus. The operation was performed at Buckingham Palace on July 15th by Sir Hugh Rigby and Mr Trotter, under general anaesthesia administered by Sir Francis Shipway. The exposed ends of the rib resected on 12th December were cut away, and a portion of the next rib was also removed, thus giving free access to the abscess cavity, which, as Dr Graham Hodgson's radiograms had suggested, was found to be circumscribed. His Majesty stood the operation very well, and both the general and local conditions are satisfactory. The immediate result of the operation is regarded as fulfilling all expectations, and we may hope that the cavity will now gradually heal up from the bottom.'

A bulletin issued from Buckingham Palace on 23rd July stated: 'During the week which has passed since the operation, His Majesty the King has made steady progress. Purulent discharge from the abscess cavity has now ceased.'

V

In the Birthday Honours issued on Monday, 3rd June 1929, the following had appeared: Lord Dawson of Penn, Privy Councillor, Sir E. Farquhar Buzzard, Baronetcy, Sir Hugh Rigby, Baronetcy, Sir Stanley Hewett, K.C.B., Sir Humphry Rolleston, G.C.V.O., Dr Francis Shipway, K.C.V.O., Dr R. S. Woods, Knighthood, Dr H. Graham Hodgson, C.V.O., Dr F. D. Howitt, C.V.O., Dr Lionel Whitby, C.V.O., and Dr Charles Dodds, the biochemist, M.V.O. Also the following nurses: Miss Catherine Black, M.B.E., Miss Rosina Davies, M.B.E., Miss Elizabeth Gordon, M.B.E., and Miss Nellie Purdie, M.B.E. There were no further honours to the King's doctors, though it is known that Mr Wilfred Trotter refused a baronetcy. Mr Henry Martyn, a general surgeon with a bias towards oto-laryngology, who practised at Windsor and was Surgeon-Apothecary to the Household, was knighted later, in 1931.

The recovery of King George V from his serious illness in 1928–29 was called at the time a triumph of 'teamwork', for thirteen doctors were in attendance at one time or another. Whether they were all necessary is another matter, and whether they all really helped to bring about recovery may be doubted. Lord Dawson, a charming and kindly man, was a medical diplomat of distinction rather than a physician of any scientific standing – the family doctor *in excelsis*. He was good-natured, genial and handsome, with jet-black hair (which owed more to Art than to Nature), and made an excellent figure-head for the medical profession, President of the British Medical Association at its Centenary Celebrations in 1932 as well as President eight times of the Royal College of Physicians of London.

When a King is the patient the inclination is always to spread the responsibility. The calling in of Sir Humphry Rolleston and Sir Farquhar Buzzard (one the Regius Professor at Cambridge and the other the Regius Professor at Oxford) did no more than this. X-ray and bacteriological examinations were, of course, necessary, but ultra-violet light treatment was a waste of time when further surgery was clearly indicated. Sir Hugh Rigby was a pleasant personality, a careful, rather diffident surgeon and he obviously was not drastic enough when he operated on King George V's empyema. After drifting on for six months with a discharging sinus, the empyema wound was cured in a week when Mr Wilfred Trotter treated the King as he would have done any other patient in hospital. As his brother-in-law Ernest Jones wrote in his autobiographical *Free Associations*, 'With Trotter rank, authority, veneration counted for nothing.'

Trotter was an unusual surgeon: elected F.R.S. for his intellectual reputation and his conception of the 'herd instinct' rather than for any original research, he wrote no textbook and made but few contributions to surgical literature. He took all surgery within his ambit, was the leading brain surgeon of his day, devised new approaches to malignant disease of the throat, was a pioneer of thyroid surgery, and a gentle and meticulous abdominal surgeon. He had little use for statistics, but he was an outstanding teacher of surgery, emphasizing fundamental principles, and he had a profound influence upon his contemporaries and especially upon his assistants and students, whom he taught to think for themselves.

REFERENCES

JOHN GORE. *King George V – a personal memoir*, John Murray, London 1941.

FRANCIS WATSON. *Dawson of Penn*, Chatto & Windus, London 1950.

SIR HAROLD NICOLSON. *King George the Fifth*, Constable, London 1952.

JAMES POPE-HENNESSY. *Queen Mary*, Allen & Unwin, London 1959.

ERNEST JONES. *Free Associations*, Hogarth Press, London 1959.

British Medical Journal: Vol. *ii*, 1928; Vols. *i* and *ii*, 1929.

The Lancet: Vol. *ii*, 1928; Vols. *i* and *ii*, 1929.

The Times: 1928–29.

CHAPTER II

POLIO AND PRESIDENT ROOSEVELT

FRANKLIN DELANO ROOSEVELT belonged to an aristocratic American family, and his mother considered that the Delanos had an even more distinguished ancestry than the Roosevelts. He was an only child, brought up at the beautiful estate of Hyde Park, on the Hudson, about half-way between Albany and New York. He had governesses and tutors at home, but at the age of 14 was sent to Groton, and had instilled into him the type of muscular Christianity with which Arnold made the reputation of Rugby. His career there was undistinguished, except that he became 'manager' of the base-ball team. He went on to Harvard in 1900, where he spent four pleasant and unexceptional years, but did not 'make Procellian' – there is nothing exactly comparable at Oxford or Cambridge, but it is like going to Eton and not being elected to 'Pop'. On the other hand, he became a successful managing editor of the well-known college journal *Crimson*.

In 1905, at the age of 23, and in the face of opposition from his mother, he married his fifth cousin once removed, Eleanor Roosevelt, an orphan. The bride was given away by her uncle Theodore, then President of the United States who, as was his way, 'stole the show' from the bride and bridegroom. The bride was not beautiful, but she was certainly attractive, intelligent, and had some private means, and people who knew them both wondered not why he married her, but why she married him. The marriage lasted for forty years and they had six children, each an individualist and high-spirited, so that one need not be surprised that there have been seven divorces in the family, and all but one of them have been married more than once.

After his marriage Franklin Roosevelt became a lawyer in New York, working as a junior for a well-known firm that were trustees for J. P. Morgan and acted for the Astor family. He felt no urge, however, to make a career at the bar, and in 1910 accepted an invitation from local politicians in Dutchess County (in which Hyde Park is situated) to stand as Democratic candidate for the New York State Senate. The Hyde Park Roosevelts were traditionally Democrats, but it caused some surprise that this wealthy young amateur should win what had long been a Republican seat. He was courageous enough at once to oppose successfully the Tammany (New York Democratic) machine in choosing a Federal Senator, and so improved his reputation both with his party and with the public.

In 1912, although he was not an official delegate, he went down to Baltimore to attend the Democratic Convention that was to nominate Woodrow Wilson as Presidential candidate, but not until the forty-sixth ballot. Roosevelt was from the first a strong Wilson supporter and made a number of important and influential friends at the convention. Among them was Josephus Daniels, who became President Woodrow Wilson's Secretary of the Navy, and offered the Assistant Secretaryship to Roosevelt, apparently because, as Daniels came from the south, he thought it judicious that his Assistant Secretary should be from the north – and also, no doubt, because the name Roosevelt meant something. He probably did not know at the time that Roosevelt's hobby was naval history. Roosevelt was tall (over six feet) and handsome, with fair hair and blue eyes, wore pince-nez and had a definite personal magnetism, but, as a columnist wrote then in the *New York Times*, 'No one would suspect behind that highly polished exterior the quiet force and determination that now are sending cold shivers down the spine of Tammany.'

This was in March 1913, and in a year or two what had been a minor government appointment became of considerable importance when the United States entered World War I, especially as Mr Daniels was more of a politician than a strategist. Most of Roosevelt's work was unspectacular – supplies, contracts, labour relations (which proved surprisingly harmonious in his hands), though he was also concerned in such active service affairs as evolving fast submarine chasers.

After the war, in 1920, Roosevelt was nominated as Democratic candidate for Vice-President, along with the hardly remembered James M. Cox from Ohio as candidate for President, but they were beaten by the Republicans Warren G. Harding and Calvin Coolidge. So when the election was over he became New York representative and vice-president of the wealthy Fidelity and Deposit Company of Maryland, with a salary of $25,000 a year. In August, 1921, he went with his family to holiday at the island of Campobello, in New Brunswick, Canada, where they had a summer home.

II

Franklin Roosevelt had had his share of illnesses, especially nose and throat troubles. At school he had three or four colds every year, a little later he complained a good deal of 'hives', probably a form of allergy (nasal allergy was to trouble him in later life); in 1912, when State Senator, he contracted typhoid fever, and in 1914 he had an operation for acute appendicitis. In 1916 he had several attacks of tonsillitis, in 1917 he had a quinsy (peritonsillar abscess), and in 1918, returning from Europe, he was attacked by pneumonia and had to be carried from the ship on a stretcher. Tonsillectomy was therefore performed on him in December, 1919, which he wrote 'has not been an agreeable operation' — he was then aged 37.

On 10th August, 1921, Roosevelt took his wife and his sons sailing at Campobello, and on their way home they saw a forest fire on one of the neighbouring islands and went ashore to fight the flames (as, according to local laws, was their duty). Then Roosevelt cooled off with a swim in a lake near by, and jog-trotted home with his sons. Later on, he swam again in the icy waters of the Bay of Fundy, then foolishly sat down in a wet bathing-suit and read his letters which had just arrived. He had a sudden chill, and his wife persuaded him to go to bed. Next day he had a high temperature and acute pain in his left leg. Mrs Roosevelt wisely sent the children away to a camp near-by, and called in the local doctor, an old friend, Dr E. H. Bennett. Dr Bennett was worried, because although his patient could walk he still had severe pain in his back and legs. By chance – ill-chance, as it turned out – a famous surgeon was spending the summer in the neighbourhood, and Dr Bennett, with Mrs Roosevelt's approval, called him in consultation. This was Dr W. W. Keen, formerly professor of surgery at the University of Pennsylvania and a pioneer of brain surgery, who, 28 years before, had helped to save the life and political reputation of President Cleveland. He examined Roosevelt on 13th August and diagnosed that 'a clot of blood from a sudden congestion had settled in the lower spinal cord, temporarily removing the power to move though not to feel'. But Roosevelt got worse in the next few days, and Dr Keen revised his diagnosis. He now decided that his patient 'had a lesion of the spinal cord'. He prescribed a course of vigorous massage and said that recovery 'might take some months'. He also sent in a bill for 600 dollars, which Mrs Roosevelt paid.

Unfortunately the famous Dr Keen was then in his 83rd year and had probably never seen a case of 'infantile paralysis', as poliomyelitis was then popularly called, in an adult before, as it affected chiefly young children. 'Vigorous' massage was about the worst form of treatment that might have been suggested, as in the early stages of poliomyelitis active movements should not be carried out, and muscles which have been fatigued in the pre-paralytic stage may have maximal paralysis later. The most severe paralysis is apt to occur in a patient who has continued his activity because the pre-paralytic stage was so slight.

During all this time Roosevelt was in pain; the sphincters of the bladder and of the bowel were paralysed and he had to be catheterized. Meanwhile his uncle, Mr Frederick Delano, talked with several doctors, who suspected from the description that the disease was 'infantile paralysis'. Mrs Roosevelt therefore insisted that a physician from Boston, Dr Robert W. Lovett, who was an authority on poliomyelitis, should be called in consultation, 'no matter what it costs'. This was two weeks after the beginning of the illness. Dr Lovett at once diagnosed the case as one of acute anterior poliomyelitis, or 'infantile paralysis', and stopped the harmful massage. Temporarily the paralysis had spread to Roosevelt's arms and back, as well as his legs.

Fortunately Louis Howe, an old friend of Roosevelt's, was a house guest at Campobello, helped Mrs Roosevelt with the nursing, and insisted that there should be as little publicity as possible. By the middle of September Dr Lovett gave permission for the patient to be moved to New York, with a prognosis that 'there was a good possibility of considerable improvement'. A private railway coach was engaged and Roosevelt was moved, with considerable difficulty, on a stretcher into the coach while onlookers were persuaded to be elsewhere. In New York Roosevelt spent six weeks at the famous Presbyterian Hospital, where an old Harvard classmate, Dr George Draper, a former associate of Dr Lovett's, looked after him. John Gunther writes that 'Draper, more than anybody except Eleanor and Howe, should have the credit for saving Roosevelt'. But when he was discharged from hospital on 28th October the medical record read, 'Not improving'.

Dr. Lovett wrote to Dr Draper (as quoted by John Gunther): 'It seems to me that it was a mild case within the range of possible complete recovery. I told them very frankly that no one could tell where they stood, that the case was evidently not of the severest type, that complete recovery or partial recovery to any point was possible, that disability was not to be feared, and that the only thing about it was the long continued character of the treatment . . . My feeling about him was that he was probably going to be a case where the conservation of what muscular power he has may be very important, and it looked to me as if some of the important muscles might be on the edge where they could be influenced either way – towards recovery, or turn into completely paralysed muscles.'

Dr Draper, in reply, wrote on 24th September to Dr Lovett: 'I feel so strongly that the psychological factor in his management is paramount. He has such courage, such ambition, and yet at the same time such an extraordinarily sensitive emotional mechanism that it will take all the skill which we can muster to lead him successfully to a recognition of what he really faces without crushing him.'

III

Acute anterior poliomyelitis, or 'polio' as it is popularly termed today, used to be called 'infantile paralysis' because it mainly affects children between the ages of two and five, though the age incidence has been rising in recent years. The old name is an unfortunate one, as 80 per cent of the cases do not become paralysed and make a complete recovery. Many persons attacked never know that they have had 'polio', and look upon it as a feverish cold. It is an acute infection by a virus of a particular group of nerve cells in the spinal cord which control the movements of certain muscles, especially of the limbs and the chest, and in severe cases the nerve cells are destroyed or partially destroyed by the virus. It is not yet known exactly how the infection is conveyed – some say in the secretions of the nose and throat, some in the excretions of the kidney or the bowel. The incubation period is 5 to 14 days, and it is commoner in the summer and autumn. The well-known vaccines that are widely used today are protective, not curative.

The disease is most serious when it is of the 'bulbar' type, when the upper part of the spinal cord nearest the brain is affected, causing paralysis of the chest muscles and the patient has to be nursed in an 'iron lung' to keep him breathing, or when there is difficulty in swallowing and laryngeal paralysis, and tracheotomy may be necessary.

It is said that persons who have undergone tonsillectomy during a poliomyelitis epidemic are more susceptible to the severe type of the disease, and – although the evidence on this is contradictory and unproven – surgeons do not nowadays do routine tonsillectomies when cases of polio are about. It has even been suggested that President Roosevelt was rendered more susceptible to the infection as he had had his tonsils operated upon – because of repeated tonsillitis and quinsy – twenty-two months before he caught the disease, but this is going much beyond any available medical evidence.

IV

His mother not unnaturally wanted Roosevelt to come up to Hyde Park after his discharge from hospital, but he and his wife insisted on going instead to their house in New York. Mrs Eleanor Roosevelt has written of the 'somewhat acrimonious dispute' about the decision to stay in New York. But the dispute was really deeper and more fundamental than that. Mrs Sara Roosevelt, the mother, wanted her disabled son to settle down to the quiet life of an invalid country gentleman at Hyde Park. Eleanor, the wife, wanted him, on the contrary, to lead an active public life, so far as this would not have a detrimental effect upon recovery, and, in particular, she felt that to resume his political career would do him good, not harm.

It has been said that his illness transformed Roosevelt from being a rather dilettante socialite and amateur politician into a serious and ambitious democratic leader, and there is a good deal of truth in that suggestion. Certainly it taught him patience and strengthened his humanitarian instincts, his sympathy with the under-dog, and during his long convalescence he was able to fill up some of the blanks in his serious reading. Mrs Eleanor Roosevelt wrote: 'Franklin's illness proved a blessing in disguise; for it gave him strength and courage he had not had before. He had to think out the fundamentals of living and learn the greatest of all lessons – infinite patience and never-ending persistence.' And when he did resume active politics, his helpless legs and awkward movements, combined with his radiant smile and vigorous gestures, gained him immediate sympathy at his public appearances. Besides, he had a beautiful voice – an actor's voice – which came over particularly well on the radio.

Miss Frances Perkins, who knew him well and became a member of his Cabinet, wrote: 'Franklin Roosevelt underwent a spiritual transformation during the years of his illness. The years of pain and suffering had purged the slightly arrogant attitude Roosevelt had displayed upon occasion before he was stricken. The man emerged completely warm-hearted with humility of spirit and a deeper philosophy.'

By the spring of 1922 Roosevelt was able to get around on crutches and exercised himself on parallel bars. He spent hours crawling on the floor and up the stairs, but the use of the muscles of his legs never came back, he was never able to walk without heavy metal braces, nor could he stand without support. But fortunately he was never discouraged and never bored.

In the autumn of 1924 his friend George Peabody, a New York banker, told Roosevelt about a warm pool, with a ramshackle hotel beside it, which he had bought, down at Warm Springs, in Georgia; Peabody had heard about a boy with infantile paralysis who had greatly improved by swimming regularly in the warm pool. Roosevelt went off at once to Warm Springs and spent six weeks there, receiving more benefit than in the previous three years. The warm pool, which had been known to the Indians as health-giving, had a constant temperature of 88 degrees Fahrenheit, and the mineral salts which the water contained made it buoyant, so that a patient could stay in it for a long time and exercise his limbs without fatigue. Roosevelt returned again and again to Warm Springs, built a house there which he named 'Little White House', then bought the whole property with the land around it and turned it into a non-profit clinic for the benefit of other polio victims, called the Georgia Warm Springs Foundation.

In June, 1924, Franklin Roosevelt re-entered political life by nominating Al Smith as candidate for the Presidency at the Democratic Convention in Madison Square Garden, New York. Roosevelt was carried on to the platform in a wheel-chair, and stood up, supported by crutches, to make the nominating speech, describing Smith in a famous phrase as 'the Happy Warrior of the political battlefield'. Al Smith was, however, a Roman Catholic (then considered politically harmful) and the nomination went to John W. Davis – who was beaten for the Presidency by Calvin Coolidge with an overwhelming majority. But the hero of the Convention was Franklin Roosevelt – he was back on the hustings again, heading for the Presidency.

REFERENCES

BASIL WOON. *Roosevelt, World Statesman*, Peter Davies, London 1942.

FRANCES PERKINS. *The Roosevelt I Knew*, Hammond, London 1946.

ELEANOR ROOSEVELT. *This I Remember*, Hutchinson, London 1950.

JOHN GUNTHER. *Roosevelt in Retrospect*, Hamilton, London 1950.

JAMES MACGREGOR BURNS. *Roosevelt: the Lion and the Fox*, Secker & Warburg, London 1956.

HELEN DIMSDALE. *Diseases of the Nervous System*, in SIR JOHN RICHARDSON'S *Practice of Medicine*, Churchill, London 1956.

NOAH D. FABRICANT. *13 Famous Patients*, Chilton, Philadelphia 1960.

RUDOLPH MARX. *The Health of the Presidents*, Putnam, New York 1960.

CHAPTER III

APPENDICITIS AND KING EDWARD VII

ONE of the most fashionable and successful surgeons in London in the early nineteen-hundreds was Sir Alfred Fripp of Guy's Hospital. His rise in Royal favour had been rapid, dating from 1890 and from a fortunate *locum tenens*, when he was first qualified, to an old Guy's man practising at York, when he had among his patients the Duke of Clarence (eldest son of the Prince of Wales, then heir to the Throne), who was serving there with his regiment. Fripp got on so well with his rather 'difficult' patient that he was asked to accompany him to Balmoral for his convalescence. His charm, tact and ability made him at once *persona grata* in Royal circles and with the wealthy Sir George Holford of the 1st Life Guards (and of Dorchester House and Westonbirt), equerry to the Duke of Clarence, who proved a good and influential friend to Fripp all his life. But he had not yet taken his F.R.C.S. (until December, 1893) and did not become assistant surgeon to Guy's Hospital until 1897 – in that same week he was appointed Surgeon-in-Ordinary to the Prince of Wales (afterwards King Edward VII), on the very same day, indeed, as the President of the Royal College of Surgeons. So that this good-looking, self-confident and highly successful young man had few friends or admirers among his senior colleagues in the world of London consultant surgeons: the only unkind remark I ever heard Sir Arbuthnot Lane make was with reference to the surgical standing of his hospital colleague Fripp.

On Sunday morning, 15th June 1902, after returning from visiting a patient, Fripp opened the front door of his beautiful house in Portland Place to encounter the waiting figure of Lord Victor Crichton, one of the equerries to King Edward VII, to whom Fripp was Surgeon-in-Ordinary. Lord Victor Crichton handed Fripp a cryptic note from Sir Francis Laking, the King's personal physician, which read: 'Come to the Royal Pavilion (Aldershot), there is a patient about whom I want your opinion.' 'Who is ill there?' he asked Crichton. 'The King,' was the answer, 'but it is very private.' For this was only ten days before the Coronation.

They hurried together to Waterloo station, but the special train which had been ordered had been moved to a siding, and when at long last it drew into the platform a telegram was handed to Crichton: 'No need for gentleman who is with you to come, patient better, he is to remain in touch.'

For the next few days he remained 'in touch' and finally wrote to Laking and was told that all was going on normally. On Tuesday, 24th June, Fripp went with some friends, at the invitation of Lord Esher, to view the interior of Westminster Abbey on the day before the Coronation. Fripp was shocked to hear a policeman saying to another visitor, 'Bless your soul, there won't be any Coronation, the King's being operated on at this moment.'

II

King Edward VII came to the throne at the mature age of 59. His mother, Queen Victoria, had kept aloof from society for nearly forty years, ever since the premature death of the Prince Consort in 1861; but she had never allowed Edward, Prince of Wales, access to confidential documents of state nor had delegated to him any of her more important responsibilities. Small wonder, therefore, that he had lived a life of pleasure, had no intellectual or literary pursuits, and was apparently interested only in sport and frivolities. He enjoyed life and luxury, and was *gourmand* as well as *gourmet*. But he had acquired a wide knowledge of men and affairs, he was intelligent as well as charming, and he never forgot a name or a face. With the man in the street he was so popular as to be called by an affectionate

C

nickname, his popularity being increased by his obvious enjoyment of horse-racing and his winning the Derby three times.

Once he had become King, he surprised his Ministers by his common sense and capacity for hard work. He had a strong sense of duty, and whatever interest he took up he applied his whole heart to it. His skill and influence as a diplomatist have been exaggerated, but his personal influence in foreign affairs was always directed towards peace. He was dignified and looked like a king, he enjoyed ceremonials, and he was genuinely interested in hospitals and their welfare, especially after his own illness and successful operation.

In 1897, when Prince of Wales, he had founded what became known later as 'King Edward's Hospital Fund', to help the hospitals of London. It still has a capital of over £9,500,000, the income of which was used on behalf of the hospitals until the advent of the National Health Service. Since the National Health Service was established in 1948 it has continued to give grants to hospitals for special purposes not covered by the Health Service, and also conducts training colleges for hospital administrators, matrons and dieticians. On the King's accession Sir Ernest Cassel gave him £200,000 to spend on some useful project of his own choice, and with it he founded the King Edward VII Sanatorium at Midhurst for middle-class patients suffering from early (and curable) tuberculosis. It was King Edward who, when he heard tuberculosis called a preventable disease, pointedly commented, 'If preventable, why not prevented?'

III

Sir Francis Laking, Physician-in-Ordinary to the King, carried out the correct medical protocol of the day when, suspecting an acute abdominal condition, he called into consultation not a surgeon but the senior physician to His Majesty, Sir Thomas Barlow of University College Hospital, an astute and knowledgeable Lancastrian. On Friday, 27th June, *The Lancet* and the *British Medical Journal*

each published articles reflecting the official medical views on the
course of the King's illness.

The Lancet said: 'On Friday, June 13th, his Majesty the King
towards the evening was suffering from great fatigue. After attending the Court and the many arduous duties of the day, he had a late
supper and went to bed, and on the following morning, Saturday
June 14th, he complained of abdominal discomforts. His Majesty
was seen during the day by Sir Francis Laking. In the afternoon he
was distinctly better. He then left for Aldershot, where he dined
with the Queen, being present in the evening at a "tattoo" held
under unfortunate atmospheric conditions [it was miserably cold
and wet]. On Saturday at midnight he complained of abdominal
pain and a feeling of distension. Sir Francis Laking was sent for, and
arrived at Aldershot at a quarter to five in the morning. Remedies
were administered, and the symptoms were all relieved. It may be
added that no morphia was given. But Sir Francis Laking recognizing the presence of an abdominal trouble that might be serious,
telegraphed for Sir Thomas Barlow, who arrived on Sunday, the
15th, and stayed there during the day. On the afternoon of Sunday
His Majesty had a "chilly fit", which in all probability amounted to
a rigor.

'On the following day, Monday, the 16th, the King proceeded
in a carriage to Windsor, adopting this method of travelling by his
physicians' advice, for it was felt by his medical advisers that if,
unfortunately, his symptoms should develop for the worse it would
be much better that he should be in his own home. The journey was
made in comfortable circumstances; he bore it well, and felt better
at the end of it. On Tuesday, the 17th, recognizing that, in view of
the approaching Coronation, no physical labour which could
possibly be avoided should be undertaken, his Majesty reluctantly
abandoned the idea of being present at Ascot. He remained recum-
bent most of the day, but drove for three-quarters of an hour in
the private grounds attached to the Castle.

'On Wednesday, the 18th, his Majesty was seen by Sir Frederick

Treves and', emphasized *The Lancet*, "'this point in the clinical history of his disease is one of the highest interest to medical men". The temperature was then elevated, there were swelling and tenderness in the right iliac fossa – in short, there were symptoms of perityphlitis. But during the following Thursday and Friday all these ominous symptoms disappeared. When Sir Frederick Treves saw his Majesty on Saturday, the 21st, his temperature had fallen and had been normal for two-and-a-half days, the swelling in the iliac region had nearly vanished, and in every way the King was much better. It was then believed that the King was on the road to rapid recovery, and that he would be able to go through the Coronation ceremonies. Sunday, the 22nd, was uneventful, and on Monday, the 23rd, the King travelled by railway from Windsor to London, his entrance to the capital being received by the public as a proof that they need attach no credence to any of the many alarming rumours that had now become widespread.'

On the Saturday (21st June) the Press Association had sent the following telegram to Sir Francis Knollys, His Majesty's private secretary: 'Persistent and alarming reports are reaching us today regarding the King's health. Can you let us state that the reports are baseless?' The following reply was received: 'Windsor Castle. – Not a word of truth in reports. – Knollys.'

IV

At this period an operation for perityphlitis, or appendicitis, was still considered a very serious one. Modern surgery dates, it is true, from the Listerian revolution (from 1867 onwards), but Lister himself never actually opened the abdomen – perhaps it was as well, for up to the end of his active surgical career he clung to the virtues of 1 in 20 carbolic acid lotion and was highly suspect of the virtues of asepsis as opposed to antisepsis. His principles transformed surgery from what it had been in the days of the Egyptians; but he made his reputation as an operating surgeon by the antiseptic treatment of compound fractures, thus avoiding hitherto inevitable amputation. The father of abdominal surgery was the truculent Lawson Tait of Birmingham, who laid down no principles, but (wrongly) never accepted the ideas of Lister, and (rightly) trusted to the virtues of soap and water and cleanliness in operating.

The name 'appendicitis' was originally given by Reginald Fitz of Boston, U.S.A., in 1888, for he was the first to recognize that it was the appendix, not the caecum, that was affected by inflammation. The first successful operation for 'recurrent typhlitis' was performed at Guy's Hospital by Sir Charters Symonds in 1883. Sir Frederick Treves performed his first deliberate operation on the appendix in 1887, but he then corrected an 'appendicular distortion' without actual excision; until 1890 he rejected the term 'appendicitis'. At the time of the illness of King Edward VII the term 'appendix' or *appendix vermiformis* was so unfamiliar that *The Times* always printed it in full in italics. But after the historic operation on the King appendicitis and the operation for its cure became increasingly fashionable on both sides of the Atlantic. The Mayo brothers, for instance, in America performed 12 operations for appendicitis in 1895, 186 in 1900 and over a thousand in 1905.

V

On the night of Monday, 23rd June, the King and Queen gave a magnificent dinner party to an imposing array of royal and princely Coronation guests. In a volume of Edwardiana edited by Mr James Laver and entitled *Edwardian Promenade* there appears a photograph of the menu of this banquet, which went as follows:

> Sherry: hot or cold consommé.
> Madeira: whitebait or trout.
> Hock: quails or roast pullets.
> Moet, 1892: saddle of lamb or Spanish ham.
> Chateau Langoa, 1874: ortolans, salad, cold asparagus.
> Tawny port,
> or 1863 port: punch gateau sprinkled with champagne.

Sherry, George IV: anchovy canapés.
1800 brandy: ices, wafers.

The guests ranged from His Imperial Highness the Hereditary Grand Duke Michael of Russia and Prince and Princess Henry of Prussia to Ras Makunan of Ethiopia and Said Ali of Zanzibar. After dinner 'the Suites in attendance upon Their Majesties' Guests had the honour of being presented to the King and Queen.'

This was altogether too much for a patient recovering from an attack of 'perityphlitis', and a relapse was almost inevitable. That night the King was in considerable pain again, his temperature rose, and he was seen by Sir Francis Laking, Sir Thomas Barlow and Sir Frederick Treves. They began (not surprisingly) to be suspicious that there might be an abscess in the right iliac region (the lower right side of the abdomen).

Next morning at a consultation at 10 o'clock, the necessity for operation became clear. Before the actual decision upon operation was arrived at Sir Frederick Treves, Serjeant-Surgeon to the King, took the advice of the two other senior Serjeant-Surgeons, Lord Lister (then aged 75), and Sir Thomas Smith (aged 70, formerly senior surgeon to St Bartholomew's Hospital), and they, as well as Sir Thomas Barlow and Sir Francis Laking, came to the unanimous conclusion that no other course but operation was possible in all the circumstances. To delay would, in fact, be to allow His Majesty to risk his life.

King Edward was obstinate and insisted: 'I must keep faith with my people and go to the Abbey.' Arguments made no headway and finally Treves said bluntly: 'Then, sir, you will go in your coffin.' The King, perhaps thinking of his friend Fripp, said to Treves, 'You will want somebody to help with this operation?' But Treves rather unkindly replied, 'Sir, you don't want the entire College of Surgeons.'

At 12.30 p.m. on Tuesday, the 24th, the operation was performed by Sir Frederick Treves. Dr Frederick Hewitt gave the anaesthetic

– the King was stout, elderly and plethoric, not a good anaesthetic risk, and soon turned deep purple. Fortunately he had a beard and this was grasped by Dr Hewitt, the royal head was pulled forwards, and the King began to breathe again (as I was told many years afterwards by Sir Frederick Hewitt himself). An incision was made by Sir Frederick Treves at the usual place, and a large abscess was opened. Pus was found at a depth of $4\frac{1}{2}$ inches and two drainage tubes of wide calibre were inserted into the appendicular abscess, surrounded by iodoform gauze. The appendix itself was not removed.

On Tuesday morning, 24th June, an official bulletin was issued from Buckingham Palace at 11.45 a.m.: 'The King is suffering from perityphlitis. His condition on Saturday was so satisfactory that it was hoped that with care His Majesty would be able to go through the Coronation ceremony. On Monday evening a recrudescence became manifest, rendering a surgical operation necessary today. (Signed) Lister, Thos. Smith, Francis H. Laking, Thos. Barlow, Fredk. Treves.

The following bulletins were subsequently issued after the operation: 'Buckingham Palace, June 24, 2 p.m. An operation on his Majesty has been successfully performed. A large abscess has been evacuated. The King has borne the operation well and is in a satisfactory condition.' (Signed) Fredk. Treves, Thos. Smith, Francis H. Laking, Thos. Barlow.

At 6 p.m. the bulletin (signed by the same physicians and surgeons) stated: 'His Majesty continues to make satisfactory progress, and has been much relieved by the operation.'

The bulletin published at 10 a.m. on the 26th stated that the King had had a restless and sleepless night in the early part of the night, but improved after 1 a.m. The later bulletin at 11 p.m. stated that he had slept for some hours during the day, had very little discomfort and was more cheerful; the wound was doing well. In fact, he sat up in bed, smoking a cigar. Sir Frederick Treves did not go to bed for seven nights, but the patient made an uninterrupted recovery.

The current issue of the *British Medical Journal* contained a report of a lecture given not long before by Sir Frederick Treves (the Cavendish Lecture to the West London Medico-Chirurgical Society) on 'Some Phases of Inflammation of the Appendix'. He said in it that 'immediate operation is demanded in every example in which there is reasonable suspicion that suppuration has taken place.' Also, that 'by the occurrence of suppuration the patient is, in all but a very small percentage of cases, cured of his trouble.'

Looking back at the detailed clinical history of the case, there is little doubt that King Edward VII owed his life to the fact that active surgical treatment was avoided until the right time, when an abscess had formed and was shut off from the abdominal cavity – nine days after he was first seen by the consultant physician, and six days after he was seen by the surgeon who operated. When a case of acute appendicitis has been diagnosed in the early stages, before perforation has occurred, it is wisest, even in the antibiotic era, to operate at once. When, however, a patient is seen by the surgeon for the first time five or six days after the onset of an attack, presenting a firm mass in the right iliac fossa, such a case does not require immediate operation. Nature has succeeded in walling off the infective focus and no immediate danger threatens the patient, though deterioration in the general condition of the patient may demand immediate operation. But if a walled-off abscess is found then and the appendix itself is not readily accessible, it would be a mistake to search for it and break down the protective adhesions.

On the news of the operation the visiting royalties at once began to make preparations to leave London, but the workmen who had not yet received contrary instructions went on preparing the grandstands and the decorations. What was to be done with the tons of food ordered for the Coronation Banquet? Some items could be kept on ice, but there were 2,500 quails, besides hundreds of chickens, partridges and sturgeons, not to mention innumerable elaborate desserts. Hampers were sent to the Little Sisters of the Poor and

other charities, and many families in the East End of London
feasted on unaccustomed dishes.

St George's Hospital, in the hope of making £10,000, had spent
over £2,000 on the erection of stands to view the procession and
had entered into a contract for some £500 worth of refreshments.
Losses on many of the commercial stands were partly covered by
insurance, but still the losses were great. Restaurants had similar
losses: Gunter's had a contract for 6,000 guests for the King's
garden party and for 1,000 luncheons at the House of Lords.
Florists and growers of flowers all over the country received a
severe blow, for few if any of them had thought of insuring.

VI

A shortened Coronation ceremony took place on 9th August, seven
weeks later. Some of the ceremonial in the Abbey was curtailed; for
instance, the sermon was omitted and the Litany was chanted in
procession before the arrival of the Royal Family. But the solemn
anointing and investing of the Sovereign in his robes, the supreme
act of placing the crown on his anointed head, the 'lifting up' of
His Majesty on to the Throne, and the homage of the Prince of
Wales and the Royal Dukes and the Peers, all carried out the ancient
ritual of the centuries for the 'sacring' of the King. 'Queen Alex-
andra,' wrote Princess Marie Louise in her reminiscences, 'was
perturbed because a drop of the Holy Oil with which she had been
anointed had trickled down on to her dear little nose, fear of irrever-
ence preventing her, as she told me, from using her handkerchief.'

Few of the foreign royalties, except those related to the King and
Queen, returned for the Coronation, but the British Empire was well
represented. There were representatives of the armed services of the
Dominions, Colonies, Dependencies and Protectorates, Maoris
from New Zealand, Dyaks from North Borneo, Chinese from
Hong Kong. The King looked well, in better health, indeed, than
the aged and feeble Archbishop of Canterbury, Dr Temple, who
had also had a recent illness and, indeed, died four months later.

The Bishop of Winchester was so alarmed at his appearance that he offered the Archbishop a meat lozenge to sustain him. 'What's the good of that,' exclaimed the Archbishop, 'my trouble's in my legs, not in my stomach.' During a long part of the ceremony he leaned heavily against the King, and when he knelt down to pray he found great difficulty in rising again. The King had to lean forward, take him by the hands, and help him up. When the ceremony was over, someone asked the King whether he was tired. 'Wonderfully enough,' he answered, 'I am not.'

Following the coronation the King had to take part in a number of fatiguing ceremonials to mark the occasion: an investiture three days later of some 1,800 Colonial troops who had taken part in the procession; on the next day an investiture of the Indian contingent; and a few days afterwards a naval review at Spithead. Then he went for a cruise among the islands of the West Coast of Scotland and returned in robust health. He lived for another eight years without any recurrence of abdominal trouble, increasingly popular with his subjects, and died of bronchitis in 1910, aged 68.

Sir Frederick Treves belonged to Dorchester, in the West of England, and was trained at the London Hospital, to which in due course he was appointed honorary surgeon. He was consulting surgeon to the Army in South Africa during the Boer War and was with the column that relieved Ladysmith. He retired from surgical practice with a fortune at the age of 55, and went to live abroad. In retirement he wrote a number of charming books of travel and reminiscence, including an unforgettable short story of London Hospital life, *The Elephant Man*.

REFERENCES

SIR FREDERICK TREVES. *The Elephant Man and other Reminiscences*, Cassell, London 1923.

SIR SIDNEY LEE. *King Edward VII: a biography*, 2 vols, Macmillan, London 1927.

CECIL ROBERTS. *Alfred Fripp*, Hutchinson, London 1932.

E. F. BENSON. *King Edward VII: an appreciation,* Longmans, London 1933.

SIR DAVID WILKIE. *Appendicitis,* in British Encyclopaedia of Medical Practice, Vol. *i,* p. 736, Butterworth, London 1936.

6TH DUKE OF PORTLAND, WILLIAM JOHN ARTHUR CHARLES JAMES CAVENDISH-BENTINCK. *Men, Women and Things: memories,* Faber, London 1937.

I. HARVEY FLACK. *Lawson Tait,* Heinemann (Medical Books), London 1949.

DOUGLAS GUTHRIE. *Lord Lister,* E. & S. Livingstone, Edinburgh 1949.

GABRIEL TSCHUMI. *Royal Chef: recollections of life in royal households from Queen Victoria to Queen Mary,* Kimber, London 1954.

W. R. BETT. *'Appendicitis,* in *The History and Conquest of Common Diseases,* University of Oklahoma Press, Norman U.S.A. 1954.

VIRGINIA COWLES. *Edward VII and his Circle,* H. Hamilton, London 1956.

H.H. PRINCESS MARIE LOUISE. *My Memories of Six Reigns,* Evans, London 1956.

JAMES LAVER. *Edwardian Promenade,* Hulton, London 1958.

British Medical Journal: Vols. *i* and *ii,* 1902.

The Lancet: Vols. *i* and *ii,* 1902.

The Times: June–August, 1902.

CHAPTER IV

THE SECRET OPERATION ON PRESIDENT CLEVELAND

GROVER CLEVELAND was twice elected President of the United States of America, in 1884 and in 1892. Cleveland was not a man of culture, but he was certainly a man of integrity, intelligence and common sense, qualities which were essential to the stability of his country during his second term of office. For in 1892 the United States was on the edge of a crisis: in that year 642 banks suspended payment, building had stopped, and unemployment was increasing. There was a loss of confidence in public credit, speculation was rampant and unwise, there was a shortage of gold in the Treasury and a real fear of a silver currency basis.

One of the first acts of the new President was to summon a special session of Congress for 7th August 1893, to repeal the Sherman Silver Purchase Act, which made it obligatory for the Government to purchase silver, at the expense of the gold reserve, which at the time was dangerously low. And in June, only a few weeks before Congress was due to meet, it was discovered that he had cancer of the upper jaw.

II

Grover Cleveland was born at Caldwell, New Jersey, where his father, a graduate of Yale, was a small-church Presbyterian minister, and his mother was the daughter of a Baltimore merchant of Irish extraction. When he was 16 his father died suddenly, and the lad became a teacher, on a pittance, in the New York State Institution for the Blind. At the end of a year he resolved to go West to seek his fortune and on the way visited an uncle who lived at Buffalo, N.Y. While staying with him he was attacked by typhoid fever and was desperately ill for weeks, attended by a Dr King, who continued afterwards to take an interest in his welfare. He became a clerk in a local law firm and at the age of 22 was admitted to the New York State bar. Next year the Civil War broke out, but the young Buffalo lawyer remained where he was, on the edge of the Canadian border, far from the field of conflict.

When Cleveland embarked on his professional career at Buffalo, a coalition machine ruled the city, first under one political party and then under the other; it was full of saloons, brothels and gambling houses, all of which contributed to both party funds. Cleveland kept clear of the local parties and attached himself to the large German community of Buffalo; in 1863 he was appointed district attorney of Erie County, but was defeated when he sought election. In 1870, however, he was elected sheriff of the same county, and won respect by his strict enforcement of the law. Such was his reputation that he was elected mayor (on a reform platform) in 1881, but before the expiry of his term of office he resigned to become Governor of New York State. In 1884 he was nominated for the Presidency of the United States on the Democratic ticket, and a bitter contest ensued with Blaine, the Republican nominee.

The revelation of an episode in his private life nearly wrecked his prospects. In 1872, an attractive widow named Maria Halpin, aged 36, gave birth to a son whom she named Oscar Folsom Cleveland after two of her great friends, Oscar Folsom and his boon companion Grover Cleveland. When a scandal-seeking opposition newspaper discovered and published this, Cleveland admitted that the allegations might well in fact be true, and that he had contributed to the support of the boy. The boy, incidentally, was placed in an orphanage, but was adopted shortly afterwards by a wealthy up-state New York family who were friends of Cleveland's. He was given a good education and became a successful professional man.

Despite the noisy opposition of the Republicans allied to the pseudo-moralists of all parties, Grover Cleveland was elected President in 1884. In office he ignored the party traditions with regard to the dispensation of patronage and political preferment and thereby antagonized many members of Congress and their 'expectant' friends. He wanted to reform the Civil Service, make appointments by examinations and by merit, and get rid of the 'spoils' system and also the scandal of pensions, which dated from the Civil War: in 1885 there were 325,000 pensioners, including dependents, and they had organized themselves into a strong society with powerful political influence. The reforms of Cleveland did not commend themselves to the selfish electors, so that he was not re-elected in 1888, being beaten by an obscure Republican, Benjamin Harrison. He resumed the practice of law in New York, but in 1892 he re-entered the arena of politics, though repeated attacks of gout prevented his making more than a few public appearances.

In the presidential election of 1892 Grover Cleveland beat both Benjamin Harrison and James B. Weaver, the nominee of the 'People's Party', who received a million votes on a platform of free coinage of silver, an income tax, abolition of national banks, and nationalization of the railways.

The Democratic Party was split on the subject of silver money: the eastern Democrats favoured hard money, the western and southern Democrats easy money; it was the old quarrel between the city and the country, between creditor and debtor. The farmers, miners and workers looked to free silver as their salvation. Cleveland favoured hard money – after all, he was an eastern Democrat – and asked Congress to repeal the Sherman Silver Purchase Act.

Only the fighting opposition of a determined president, it was generally conceded, could steady a vacillating Congress, oppose the leaders of his own party, and save financial panic. Vice-President Adlai Stevenson (grandfather of his namesake of today) was the nominee of the 'silver wing' of the party, and if he did not actually favour the Act at least he did not oppose it. But President Cleveland accepted the challenge and fought the silver advocates with every political weapon that he could command. *The Commercial and Financial Chronicle* commented: 'Mr Cleveland is about all that stands between this country and absolute disaster: his death would be a great calamity.'

III

Such was the situation when it was discovered on the 18th June that the President had malignant disease of the upper jaw. His doctor in Washington, Dr R. M. O'Reilly, later Surgeon-General of the U.S. Army, found a rough spot on the President's hard palate and sent a tissue specimen (without disclosing the patient's name) to the Army Medical Service pathologist, who reported that he suspected a malignant condition. Dr. William H. Welch of Johns Hopkins Hospital, Baltimore, the leading pathologist in America, confirmed the diagnosis. The surface of the growth was about the size of a shilling (a quarter-dollar) and extended on the left side from the bicuspid teeth to within one-third of an inch of the soft palate. It was found to have invaded the overlying bone of the upper jaw. Dr O'Reilly called in Dr Joseph D. Bryant of New York, a well-known surgeon and personal friend of the President, who said: 'Were it in my mouth, I would have the growth removed at once.'

The President was 56 years old, of corpulent build, and with a short, thick neck – hardly the best subject for the general anaesthetics used at that time. Mr Cleveland authorized Dr Bryant to go ahead with the necessary preparations, but enjoined the greatest secrecy on the part of all concerned. Dr W. W. Keen of Philadelphia, doyen of American surgeons, author of a five-volume textbook of surgery and a pioneer of brain surgery, was called in to help, and to 'assume responsibility, in part, in the event of a fatality', as Dr Bryant said to his assistant, Dr Erdmann.

On 26th June, Secretary of War Lamont, who was in the President's confidence, was informed that on Wednesday or Thursday the yacht *Oneida*, owned by Mr E. C. Benedict, a devoted friend of President Cleveland, would be standing by Pier A, New York, to receive 'our friend, who should go aboard on Friday night or at all events Saturday.'

Aboard the yacht Dr Bryant, Secretary of War Lamont, and the President found Mr Benedict and Drs O'Reilly, Janeway (a leading New York physician), Hasbrouck (a well-known dentist), Erdmann (Bryant's regular assistant), and Keen, who had all arrived separately and at different times of the day. The operation was scheduled for next day and meanwhile the President was given a careful general medical examination by Dr Janeway. He slept well that night without sedatives. The yacht remained anchored in Bellevue Bay and next day steamed slowly up the East River. As it passed Bellevue Hospital, on the edge of the Manhattan Island bank of the river, all of the doctors left the deck in case they might be recognized by some of the staff of the Hospital.

The President was propped up in the cabin on a chair against the ship's mast and administration of the anaesthetic began – first, nitrous oxide until he became unconscious, and then ether, given by Dr O'Reilly. Dr Hasbrouck extracted the two left upper bicuspid teeth, and then Dr Bryant made incisions in the roof of the mouth and began excision of the upper jaw, the orbital plate (the floor of the bony cavity which contains the eyeball) being left intact. A small portion of the soft palate was removed, but no external excision was made, a large cheek retractor being used. The entire left upper jaw was removed, from the first bicuspid tooth to just beyond the last molar tooth. The maxillary antrum was found to be occupied by a gelatinous mass which was considered then to be a sarcoma, but later on (according to Dr Erdmann) on microscopical examination was found to be a carcinoma, as is indeed the more usual and the more likely from the descriptions. One blood-vessel only was tied, the wound was tightly packed with gauze and haemorrhage was slight, the galvano-cautery being used at but one point. Only about six ounces of blood were lost. At the end of the operation the patient's pulse-rate was a normal 80. The post-operative course was uneventful, the temperature never rising above 100° F.

Two days later the President was up and about and on 5th July, when *Oneida* dropped anchor at Buzzards Bay, Cape Cod, he was able to walk off the yacht to his summer home at Gray Gables. On 17th July there was a minor operation, again on board the yacht *Oneida*, to remove some suspicious-looking tissue at the edge of the wound, and the surface was cauterized with the galvano-cautery. When the packing was removed speech was unintelligible, but an excellent prosthesis of vulcanized rubber was made by Dr Kasson C. Gibson, a New York dentist, which gave the face a normal appearance and the voice a natural quality. By the end of July the President was able to resume his normal activities, and on 5th August 1893, just twenty days after the operation, he arrived in Washington to direct political strategy. The Sherman Law was repealed, and the purpose of the secrecy had been achieved.

III

For nearly two months the operation remained a complete secret, and then on 29th August a reporter published in the *Philadelphia Press* a detailed account of the whole affair, but everywhere the story was met with disbelief. An intimate friend of the President's, Clarke Davis, editor of the *Philadelphia Public Ledger*, issued a signed statement that the story had only 'the basis of a toothache', and 'Mr Cleveland's closest friends do not know of any other.' Dr Bryant blamed Dr Hasbrouck, the dentist, for the leak, and never spoke to him again – he even sent him his fee of 250 dollars by a messenger, without any note of thanks.

Recently, however, Dr Joseph M. Miller of Baltimore has shown Dr Hasbrouck in a more favourable light. The reporter of the *Philadelphia Press*, Elisha J. Edwards, was a close friend of Dr Leander P. Jones of Greenwich, Connecticut, the family doctor of Commodore Benedict and of Andrew Carnegie. Dr Jones had a patient who required an operation and the surgeon engaged to perform it recommended as anaesthetist Dr Hasbrouck, who was an expert on the administration of nitrous oxide. An appointment was made, but Dr Jones and the surgeon waited in vain for an hour or two for Dr Hasbrouck; they tried to contact him, but learned only that he had gone away. The operation had to be postponed, and next day a telegram was received from Hasbrouck that he had been unavoidably detained but would return as soon as possible. When he finally arrived he told the story of the operation on President Cleveland in order to give an adequate excuse for his inexplicable absence. Dr Leander P. Jones related the story to Elisha Edwards with some indignation, and as it was then evident that the Sherman Silver Act would be repealed, the reporter thought that it would do no harm to make it public.

When eventually he retired from politics, respected and honoured, Grover Cleveland went to live at Princeton, New Jersey, where he occasionally lectured on public affairs and was elected a Trustee of the University. In June 1908, he died — according to the death certificate, of 'heart failure, complicated with pulmonary thrombosis and oedema' — without any recurrence of the malignant condition for which he had undergone his secret operation fifteen years previously. The facts were not generally known until in the *Saturday Evening Post* of 22nd September 1917, Dr W. W. Keen, then 80 years old, published a detailed account of the operation and of the circumstances under which it was performed, 24 years after the operation, and nine years after the death of Grover Cleveland.

REFERENCES

HENRY JONES FORD. *The Cleveland Era,* Yale University Press, New Haven 1905.

W. W. KEEN. *The Surgical Operations on President Cleveland, and six other papers of reminiscences,* Lippincott, New York 1928.

ALLAN NEVINS. *Grover Cleveland, a Study in Courage,* Dodd, Mead & Co, New York 1933.

D. W. BROGAN. *Government of the People — a study of the American political system,* Harper, New York 1933.

M. G. SEELIG. Surgery, Gynecology and Obstetrics, Vol. 85, p. 373. 1947.

ANDRÉ MAUROIS. *Grover Cleveland and his time* – Chapter XLVI in *A New History of the United States*, John Lane, London 1948.

P. M. DALE. *Medical Biographies: the ailments of 33 famous persons*, Norman, Oklahoma 1952.

JOSEPH M. MILLER. Surgery, Gynecology and Obstetrics, Vol. 113, p. 524. 1961.

CHAPTER V

THE CASE OF THE EMPEROR FREDERICK

THE case of the Emperor Frederick III of Germany was a turning point in European history. It all took place seventy-five years ago, when the reign of the aged first Emperor of Germany was drawing to a close, and the dawn of a possible liberal Germany became apparent, for it was encouraged with active sympathy by the Crown Prince Frederick and his English wife, daughter of Queen Victoria and the favourite child of the Prince Consort.

A Germany possessing a genuinely liberal outlook might well have taken a high place of honour among the nations of the world, with peace, contentment and prosperity, and two great wars and years of conflict and bitterness might well have been avoided. But the Emperor Frederick III was to reign, a sick man, for ninety-nine days only, giving the world a mere glimpse of what might have been, and with the wayward and ambitious rule of his son, the Emperor William II, in his place, reaction took the place of liberalism.

II

Prince Frederick William of Prussia, afterwards the German Crown Prince and Emperor Frederick III, was born on 18th October, 1831, the eldest son of Prince William of Prussia, who became the first German Emperor at Versailles in January, 1871, and lived until he was 82. Prince Frederick William was educated by tutors and at the University of Bonn, but he was brought up as a soldier and never forgot that one day he should be Commander-in-chief of the Prussian Army. Queen Victoria described him as follows: 'The Crown Prince hates intrigue and is very straightforward and honest and kind-hearted, but rather weak and to a certain extent obstinate, not conceited but absurdly proud, as all his family are, thinking no family higher or greater than the Hohenzollerns.'

A Crown Prince often has a viewpoint different from his father's, and in the case of Prince Frederick William this was notorious, for he favoured the political opponents of Bismarck, his father's Chancellor, and his palace was frequented by writers, artists, historians, scientists, and the Liberal parliamentary leaders. The Prince had developed his liberal attitude on a visit to England in 1851, when he came under the kindly influence of the Prince Consort. He also fell in love with his eldest daughter, 'Vicky', an intelligent and attractive girl, with whom the Prince Consort was accustomed to discuss current international problems, and married her in 1858.

Bismarck hated the influence of the Crown Princess, who was said to be 'very pro-English in Berlin and very pro-German in London'. For in the eyes of Bismarck England had been on the 'downward course' ever since 1832, and although he was called 'the Great State Socialist' because of his programme of social reform – sickness, accident, and old age State insurance – which he devised as a bulwark against socialism, he disliked and distrusted parliamentary government on the English model, with a ministry responsible to the chamber.

In the Franco–Prussian War of 1870–71 Prince Frederick William was in command of the Third Army, composed of Prussians, Bavarians, Wurttemburgers and Hessians, and made a reputation both for military ability and for clemency, for he opposed the bombardment of Paris after Napoleon III had surrendered with his army at Sedan. It was in front of Paris that Bismarck said, 'Prisoners: why do they continue to take prisoners? They should have shot down the whole of them, one after another.' The Crown Prince would hardly have been human if he had not felt frustrated at having to wait so long for the throne and found himself instead appointed to such a mildly decorative post as 'Protector of Public Museums', visited the Prado in Madrid and the galleries in Florence, Rome and Venice, and attended the ceremonial opening of the Suez Canal. But in 1885, when the aged Emperor William's health was giving rise to some anxiety, the Crown Prince asked Bismarck whether, in case of a change of monarchy, he would remain in office. Bismarck declared that he was ready to do so under two conditions: 'No parliamentary government and no foreign influence in politics.' The Crown Prince, with a gesture of reassurance, answered: 'Not a thought of that.' At least, so says Bismarck in his memoirs.

It was in January 1887, that the Crown Prince Frederick, then 55 years old, began to show evidence of slight but persistent hoarseness. This was assumed to be of catarrhal origin, for he had caught a severe cold in the north of Italy in the autumn of 1886, when one evening he went for a drive in the country and the coachman lost his way; it became dark and chilly, and the Crown Prince had no greatcoat with him. For the next month or two, however, no cough or other signs of catarrh were present, and inhalations and other medicines for catarrh did not bring about any improvement in the hoarseness. On 6th March, 1887, therefore, Dr Wegner, the Crown Prince's Physician-in-Ordinary, who was Deputy Medical Director-General in the German Army, called into consultation Dr Gerhardt, Professor of Clinical Medicine at the University of Berlin, who was also a well-known authority on diseases of the throat, for laryngologists then were also physicians. On examination with the laryngoscope Professor Gerhardt found that the Crown Prince had, on his left vocal cord, 'a long, low somewhat uneven pale-red little nodule, about four millimetres in length and two millimetres in height'. The vocal cords moved quite easily in the act of phonation. The diagnosis he made was that of a polypoid thickening of the left vocal cord, for it was a thickening rather than an out-growth from the vocal cord.

Having applied a 20 per cent solution of cocaine to the larynx Professor Gerhardt attempted to remove the nodule with a snare, but this brought away only a tiny fragment. A ring-knife also failed, so Gerhardt burned away the greater part of the thickening with the galvano-cautery, which he applied no fewer than thirteen times. The surface did not heal after these cauterizations, so that Gerhardt began to have a vague suspicion that this might be a more serious condition, which he mentioned to Dr Wegner. He was relieved, however, to see that both vocal cords moved equally freely, for at that time – and, indeed, for many years later – lack of mobility in a vocal cord was considered one of the earliest signs of cancer of the larynx. It is now known to be a comparatively late sign of the presence of cancer of a vocal cord, caused by infiltration of the cancer into it, though it may be caused by other conditions.

The Crown Prince was then sent to the spa of Ems for two weeks, for rest to the voice, inhalations and douches for the nose and throat. There his cough improved, the irritation, swelling and redness of the larynx subsided, his spirits were much better, and he ate, slept and looked well. When, however, the Crown Prince returned to Berlin on 15th May, Professor Gerhardt did not find any signs of real improvement, the hoarseness was even more marked, the movement of the left vocal cord was sluggish, and the surface of the little tumour was still not healed. Gerhardt therefore asked for a second opinion, pressing for a consultation with Professor von Bergmann, professor of surgery in the University of Berlin.

Professor von Bergmann examined the Crown Prince on 16th May and immediately advised that on account of possible cancer the operation of laryngo-fissure, or splitting the larynx from the front of the neck, should be undertaken, for the purpose of exploration and if necessary removal of the growth. Professor von Bergmann gave this advice entirely on the history of the case and relying on the description given by Gerhardt, for he was no laryngologist and had had no experience in using the laryngeal mirror. According to Dr Wegner, von Bergmann said: 'Gerhardt makes the diagnosis, I am only the operator.' This attitude as between physician and surgeon was, of course, not unknown much later than the eighteen-eighties. Professor Ernst von Bergmann was an early follower of Lister and developed 'aseptic' as an improvement on Lister's 'antiseptic' surgery. It was he who introduced sterilization by steam, and he was widely recognized as one of the leading surgeons in Europe.

After this consultation between Professors Gerhardt and von Bergmann, Dr Wegner brought up the subject of having a laryngologist in consultation also. Gerhardt wrote afterwards that he and von Bergmann agreed to this as they considered that the laryngoscopic appearance of the larynx and the history of the illness would convince anyone who knew anything about laryngology to come to the same conclusion. Several names were mentioned, in particular Professor Moure of Bordeaux and Professor von Schrötter of Vienna, and after due consideration it was decided to call in Dr Morell Mackenzie of London, the German translation of whose classical textbook Wegner was reading at the time, and with whom Professor Gerhardt was personally acquainted. Mackenzie had, in fact, been president of the section of laryngology at the International Medical Congress in Copenhagen in 1884.

Morell Mackenzie was the son of a doctor at Leytonstone, Essex, who was killed in an accident, and was educated at the medical school of the London Hospital, qualifying as a doctor in 1858. A generous aunt not only paid his fees there, but sent him for postgraduate study to Paris, Vienna and Buda-Pest, and in Buda-Pest he met his destiny, for there in 1859 Professor Czermak was introducing into practical medicine the newly invented laryngoscope, the simple yet magical mirror that showed for the first time to the eyes of man the interior of the larynx and the working of the vocal cords. It was Manuel Garcia, a Spanish teacher of singing living in London, who first was successful, in 1854, in examining his own larynx with the aid of a dental mirror; and it was Professor Türck of Vienna who first used laryngeal mirrors in the wards of a hospital, but he put them aside as useless, for he had trusted to the sunlight for illumination, which was inadequate.

When Morell Mackenzie returned from the Continent he was appointed in turn Resident Medical Officer and then Medical Registrar at the London Hospital, and started practice as a physician in 1862. In that same year he founded a dispensary for diseases of the throat, which later became the Throat Hospital, Golden Square, with beds for in-patients, the first in the world. Mackenzie did not call himself a laryngologist – he was a physician with a special interest in diseases of the throat. He had clever hands and by constant practice made himself the most skilful laryngologist in Europe. Cocaine was not introduced into medicine until 1880 and into laryngology as a local anaesthetic in 1884; yet by 1871 Mackenzie had published a monograph on 100 growths which he had removed from the larynx with incredible dexterity without any anaesthetic, local or general.

In 1866 Mackenzie was appointed to the honorary staff of the London Hospital, and in 1870, at the age of 33, he took a lease of No. 19 Harley Street, one of the largest houses in that street. He had an enormous practice, taught hundreds of doctors from all over the world the elements of laryngology at his hospital, wrote the classical textbook on diseases of the nose and throat, in two volumes, published in 1880 and 1884, and in 1887 founded the *Journal of Laryngology*. He was not, therefore, either 'unknown' or 'undistinguished', as was suggested later by the Germans.

Meanwhile, arrangements were going forward for the operation on the Crown Prince, without either the reigning Emperor or his Chancellor having been informed, and when Bismarck found out about this another consultation was ordered for 18th May. At this consultation there were present, besides Gerhardt, von Bergmann and Wegner, the surgeon-in-ordinary to the Crown Prince and the physician-in-ordinary to the Emperor, with Professor Tobold, a senior Berlin laryngologist. Tobold examined the Crown Prince's larynx carefully with the laryngoscope, and told the other doctors in an adjoining room that the condition 'could be considered cancer without any other diagnosis'. It was then unanimously agreed to recommend that the larynx should be opened by laryngo-fissure and the growth removed. Dr Eugen Hahn, a well-known Berlin laryngologist, was to assist Professor von Bergmann. The operation was fixed for 7 a.m. on the morning of 21st May, in the New Palace at Potsdam, an operating table was brought from the Charité Hospital in Berlin, and two trained nurses were engaged.

On the 18th May, after the second consultation, a telegram was sent to Dr Morell Mackenzie in London, inviting him to come at once to a consultation in Berlin with the German doctors who were attending the Crown Prince. This was reinforced by a telegram from the Crown Princess to Queen Victoria, who sent her personal physician, Dr James Reid, to call on Morell Mackenzie at his house in Harley Street, urging him to start as soon as possible.

III

The summons to Mackenzie has given rise to acrimonious arguments and discussions, for it was universally assumed in Germany – and not discouraged by the newspapers or by Bismarck himself – that the English Crown Princess was responsible for bringing the English laryngologist to Berlin. But the official German gazette and the official medical report later both stated that it was the Crown Prince's medical attendants who were responsible, and in a personal letter of thanks to Mackenzie towards the end of the case the Crown Prince wrote: 'You were called to me by the unanimous wish of my German medical attendants. Not knowing you myself, I had confidence in you in consequence of their recommendation. But I soon learned to appreciate you from personal experience.'

Morell Mackenzie arrived in Berlin on the afternoon of 20th May and drove at once to the New Palace, where rooms had been prepared for him. After being presented to the Crown Prince, he conferred with the group of doctors already in attendance, among whom he was surprised to find that the only laryngologist was

Professor Tobold, now almost in retirement. Dr Wegner and Professor Gerhardt then gave the history of the case in detail, following which Mackenzie took the Crown Prince into a darkened room and made a careful examination of his throat with a laryngeal mirror. He found a growth about the size of a split pea at the posterior part of the left vocal cord; it was of a pale pink colour, slightly rough on the surface, but not lobulated. On phonation a portion of the growth disappeared from view, showing that it was partly attached to the under-surface of the vocal cord. There was no trace of ulceration on the growth, which to the naked eye bore the look of a simple wart or papilloma. The affected vocal cord did not move so freely as its fellow on the right side. Except for the loss of voice, the throat gave the Crown Prince no trouble – no pain, no difficulty in breathing, no hindrance to swallowing.

From a sketch by Dr Morell Mackenzie of the Crown Prince's larynx when first seen (from Sir Morell Mackenzie: *Frederick the Noble*, London, Sampson Low, 1888, page 13).

Mackenzie then withdrew to discuss the case with his colleagues, and pointed out that the conclusion that had been arrived at seemed to him to be on insufficient grounds, and that the most obvious means of arriving at a correct diagnosis was to remove a small piece of the growth by way of the throat and have it examined microscopically by an expert pathologist. According to the German official report later, Mackenzie stated that 'he was opposed to an external operation until by such an examination the cancerous nature of the growth had been established.'

In making this recommendation for biopsy, Mackenzie was on sure ground – in fact, he was well in advance of the general medical opinion of his day; and today no laryngologist would approve a major operation on the larynx without a biopsy. But there are definite rules that should be observed in biopsy: there must be an ample amount of tissue, it must be taken with precision, and if inconclusive the biopsy should be repeated.

Next morning all the doctors assembled again at the Palace and, having cocainized the Crown Prince's larynx, Mackenzie removed a small piece of the growth with laryngeal forceps. This was at once sent to Professor Rudolf Virchow, who was professor of pathology at Berlin University and, indeed, the founder of modern cellular pathology.

Professor Virchow's report on the first specimen, which was subsequently published in the *Berliner Klinische Wochenschrift*, was non-commital: 'A very superficial piece of mucous membrane had been removed, to which at one spot only a somewhat irregular shred of deeper tissue adhered. In a few spaces, nests of epithelial cells had originated. Thus nothing was found that contradicted a simple irritative process.' Virchow told Wegner verbally that the affection might be *pachydermia laryngis* – a thickened warty condition resulting from chronic inflammation, which in fact he had been the first to describe and name. This is the condition long afterwards described by Chevalier Jackson as 'contact ulcer' of the larynx. Virchow emphasized his opinion by lecturing on 'Pachydermia laryngis' at the Berlin Medical Society on 27th June, letting it be understood that he was taking the case of the Crown Prince as his text.

On 8th June, Mackenzie removed a second specimen, and Virchow now reported: 'A more central portion of the growth has apparently been obtained. Although this portion shows marked disease, yet the healthy condition of the tissue on the cut surface allows a very favourable opinion to be formed as to prognosis. Whether such an opinion would be justified in respect of the whole disease cannot be ascertained with certainty from the two portions removed. However, there is nothing present in them which would be likely to arouse the suspicion of wider and graver disease.'

After the reading of Virchow's report a general discussion took place among the doctors, the result being that, with the unanimous consent of all those present, the Crown Prince was handed over to Morell Mackenzie for treatment. The Crown Prince was extremely anxious to ride in Queen Victoria's Jubilee procession in London and to be present at the religious service of thanksgiving at Westminster Abbey, which was scheduled for 21st June. He therefore went with Mackenzie, Dr Wegner and Gerhardt's assistant, Dr Landgraf, to London on 14th June, living quietly at a suburban hotel.

On 28th June Mackenzie removed a third specimen from the Crown Prince's larynx and sent it for microscopic examination. Virchow's detailed report was subsequently printed in full in the *British Medical Journal* – its conclusion ran as follows: 'No deep layers of tissue, as after the first, and still more the second operation, had been removed. The section had been made very near the surface, so that only mucous membrane was removed. Thus only a little tissue, and that difficult to handle, was afforded for the purpose of an opinion on the structure of the underlying parts. No alveolar structure, or deposition, or penetration of epithelial masses could anywhere be perceived in this tissue. It consisted of young connective tissue, which had increased not towards the deeper part, but towards the surface, and contained elements some of which were proliferating. Nowhere did this proliferation reach the character of an independent centre of formation. Thus this excised portion, in a still higher degree than was the case with the portions obtained by the previous operations, has shown itself to be a hard, compressed warty growth, that has started, from a moderately irritated and thickening surface, and the examination of its base has not afforded the least support for the idea of a new formation penetrating inwards.'

Thus there was quite definitely no microscopic evidence of malignancy, although of the three specimens examined only the second was really a satisfactory one.

After the Jubilee festivities the Crown Prince and Princess went first to the Isle of Wight and then on to Braemar, in the Scottish Highlands, close to Queen Victoria at Balmoral. At Braemar on 2nd August and again on the 7th Mackenzie applied a galvano-cautery to remove a small recurrence of the growth on the left vocal cord. It healed completely and this growth never returned. Queen Victoria was delighted to hear the Crown Prince's 'natural voice again', and on 7th September she invited Morell Mackenzie to luncheon at Balmoral and knighted him immediately afterwards in the drawing-room.

IV

It was now decided that the Crown Prince had better stay away from Berlin for the winter, and a villa was taken for him at San Remo, on the Italian Riviera, where the Prince and Princess with their entourage arrived on 3rd November. They were accompanied by Mr Mark Hovell, Mackenzie's assistant and staunch friend – from whose lips many years afterwards I was to get much of my first-hand information regarding the case.

Within twenty-four hours of arrival Mark Hovell sent an urgent telegram to Morell Mackenzie, who arrived from London on the evening of 5th November. Next morning, when he examined the larynx, he found the left arytenoid (behind and above the vocal cord) swollen and bright pink, and a sub-glottic tumour half an inch below the left vocal cord, with a smaller one below the right cord. Its appearance was altogether unlike the other swellings which had shown themselves in the larynx, and in Mackenzie's opinion 'had in fact a distinctly malignant look'. He told the Crown Prince that a very unfavourable change had taken place in his throat. He asked: 'Is it cancer?' To which Mackenzie replied: 'I am sorry to say, sir, it looks very much like it, but it is impossible to be certain.'

Thirty newspaper correspondents from all over the world poured into San Remo, sat watching every movement at the villa with field-glasses or telescopes, and constantly badgered Mackenzie at his hotel. The staff at the local telegraph office had to be doubled. The reports in even such a sedate newspaper as the London *Times* show that it would have had little to learn from the most persistent and thick-skinned columnist of today.

On 9th November consultations were held between Mackenzie and Hovell and the eminent laryngologists Professor von Schrötter from Vienna and Dr Krause from Berlin, and next day also with Dr Moritz Schmidt, a well-known laryngologist from Frankfurt, who had arrived in company with Prince William, with instructions to report on the case direct to the Emperor. After examining the larynx Dr Moritz Schmidt urged that large doses of potassium iodide should be given, to which the others agreed that there could be no harm in trying that drug. When Dr Moritz Schmidt got back to Frankfurt he stated publicly, in a lecture at the university, that in his opinion the disease from which the Crown Prince was suffering was 'of contagious origin', i.e. syphilis.

Nevertheless, on the next day the doctors decided that the Crown Prince should be formally made acquainted with their views at a personal interview, and that Professor von Schrötter of Vienna should be their spokesman. Though von Schrötter did not actually use the word 'cancer', he made it perfectly clear that he and his colleagues believed the condition to be malignant and explained the alternatives in the way of treatment. The Crown Prince, after reflection, sent them a written communication that he declined to have his larynx excised, but would submit to tracheotomy should it become necessary. On 28th November, Drs Krause and Hovell reported to Mackenzie, who had returned to London: 'There is now no ulceration to be seen. The part of the growth which first appeared is smaller and smoother. There is now a cicatrix on the portion of the ventricular band formerly occupied by an ulcer . . . During the last week or ten days the enlargement of the glands has materially diminished.'

A month later Mackenzie was recalled by an urgent telegram: 'Sudden increase of growth.' When, however, he examined the larynx on 15th December he said although there were some small white vegetations on the left ventricular band, that he could find no dangerous signs or symptoms, and on 17th December the following bulletin was issued: 'On the left half of the larynx of the Crown Prince there is now visible a small growth situated a little higher up than the swelling which appeared at the end of October and which, partially cicatrized as it is, has decreased in size. The Crown Prince's general condition appears to be good.' Morell Mackenzie, telegraphing to Dr Reid, was rather more precise: 'Small new growth on left ventricular band, does not look malignant, general appearance of larynx much more favourable than it was beginning of November.'

On 17th January, 1888, the Crown Prince expectorated a large slough (nearly 2 inches long, $\frac{1}{2}$ inch wide, $\frac{1}{8}$ inch thick, with two other smaller pieces), which Professor Virchow reported to be a necrosed part of the inner surface of the larynx, without any cartilage present in it; no mention was made of any suspicion of cancer in the specimen. Morell Mackenzie reported on 29th January: 'Below the left cord was a red, slightly raised scar, below the right cord a swelling.' On 7th February he reported that 'At present there are no indications for tracheotomy'; but on 9th February he found that the whole of the left side of the larynx was very much swollen and inflamed, on the right side the sub-glottic region red and swollen.

In view of this finding Mackenzie urged that tracheotomy should be performed forthwith, and at 3 p.m. that afternoon this was done under general anaesthesia in the drawing-room by Dr Bramann,

Professor von Bergmann's assistant, who had been sent to San Remo in case of emergency. The swelling in the larynx settled down after the tracheotomy, and the Crown Prince was soon up and about again. At his request Mackenzie drew up a report for the Emperor, which was also published in the leading medical journals on 18th February. In it Mackenzie wrote: 'The general idea is that I am of opinion that the disease from which His Imperial Highness is suffering is not cancer; the view, on the other hand, which I have consistently maintained, is that there never has been any proof of the existence of cancer.' After giving details of the course of the case and Professor Virchow's reports, the statement ended: 'In my opinion, the clinical symptoms have always been entirely compatible with non-malignant disease, and the microscopic signs have been in harmony with this view. I need only add that, although in nearly every case of laryngeal disease it is possible at the first inspection to form an accurate opinion as to the nature of the disease presenting itself, yet in a few rare instances the progress of the complaint alone permits its character to be determined. Unfortunately, the case of His Imperial Highness is among the latter number, and at this moment medical science does not permit me to affirm that any other disease is present than chronic interstitial inflammation of the larynx combined with perichondritis.'

V

On 9th March the aged Emperor William I died, and the Crown Prince, now the Emperor Frederick III, with his Empress, and accompanied by Mackenzie and Mark Hovell, returned to Berlin in a special train, arriving in a blinding snowstorm. For the sake of quiet and privacy they went to the small palace of Charlottenburg, situated in a large park in a western suburb of Berlin, instead of to one of the more public royal residences in Berlin or Potsdam.

Spring came suddenly that year, and on 29th March the Emperor and Empress were able to go out for a drive in an open carriage. Next day they drove into Berlin along Unter den Linden amid

E

enthusiastic holiday crowds, followed by some of the Household
officers, including Mackenzie, in other carriages.

On 3rd April the Emperor said that he felt better than he had
done since the tracheotomy, but on 12th April an incident occurred
which deepened the antagonism between the German and the
English doctors. The tracheotomy tube had been causing some discomfort, so Mackenzie resolved to change it for another with a
different curve. As the tracheotomy was a surgical affair under the
general control of Professor von Bergmann, Mackenzie thought that
he ought to be present when a new tube was inserted, and asked him
to come out to Charlottenburg 'as soon as possible'. Von Bergmann
arrived in a state of excitement, thinking that an emergency had
arisen, and in inserting the new tube made a false passage and
damaged the tissues of the neck, causing some bleeding and pain.
A few days later the Emperor had bronchitis with fever, and an
abscess formed and burst in front of the trachea, which Mackenzie
justifiably blamed for subsequent developments due to sepsis.

On 6th June a statement was published that the health of the
Emperor continued to be so satisfactory that in future bulletins
would be issued only at the discretion of the doctors, but only two
days later Mackenzie found that a much-dreaded fistula had mani-
fested itself – liquids were sometimes passing from the oesophagus
into the larynx, through an ulcerated opening. This was a most
serious complication, and Mackenzie had to introduce a tampon-
cannula to prevent the liquids from trickling down into the trachea.

On 12th June Mackenzie telegraphed to Dr Reid: 'The Emperor
is rapidly losing ground,' and on 15th June, at eleven o'clock in the
morning, the Emperor Frederick III died, having reigned for ninety-
nine days.

VI

Next day, Bismarck, the Chancellor, asked for a report on the case
of the Emperor, and Mackenzie therefore wrote out at once the
following statement: 'Schloss Friedrichskron, June 16th, 1888. It

is my opinion that the disease from which the Emperor Friedrich III died was cancer. The morbid process probably commenced in the deeper tissues and the cartilaginous structure of the larynx became affected at a very early date. A small growth which was present when I first examined the late Emperor was removed by me by several endolaryngeal operations, and though all the portions taken away were submitted to Professor Virchow, he was unable to detect in them any evidence of the existence of cancer. Examination of the sputa made at the beginning of March by Professor Waldeyer, however, led that pathologist to believe that cancer was then present. Whether the disease was originally cancerous or assumed a malignant character some months after its first appearance, it is impossible to state. The fact that perichondritis and caries of the cartilages played an active part in the development of the disease no doubt largely contributed to make it impossible to form a decided opinion as to its nature till quite recently.'

A post-mortem examination was carried out by Professor Virchow, assisted by Professor Waldeyer, in the presence of Morell Mackenzie, Hovell, Professor von Bergmann, and two or three other physicians. The examination was hurried, for the lying-in-state had been arranged to begin within an hour, and Virchow stated afterwards that it was to be regretted that more care and time had not been given to the drawing up of the protocol on the post-mortem examination. The neck, larynx and lungs alone were examined, and the larynx, upper part of the trachea and oesophagus, were ligatured and removed. It was found that nearly the whole of the larynx (except the epiglottis and ary-epiglottic folds) had been destroyed and it now consisted of a large flat gangrenous ulcer; patches of septic broncho-pneumonia were present in the lungs; no mention was made of any abscess cavity. There was no trace of perforation of the oesophagus.

At the base of the epiglottis, on the left side, was a nodule as large as a cherry, and near it were several similar nodules of various sizes, but all much smaller than the first one. On the left side of the neck, close to the jugular vein, was a lymphatic gland about as large as a pigeon's egg, 'which in its interior showed a medullary-looking yellow spot'. These naked-eye appearances were apparently held to be enough to warrant a diagnosis of cancer of the larynx!

Professor Virchow and Waldeyer subsequently reported their microscopic findings. The nodule at the base of the epiglottis contained an alveolar structure with epidermoidal contents, among which were 'nest-cells'. The cutaneous nodule removed from the neck also contained 'nest-cells'. The lymphatic gland, however, showed the highest degree of change, the normal structure being 'replaced by a loose alveolar tissue, the spaces of which are closely filled with epidermoidal cells having large nuclei'. No mention is made of any microscopical examination of any other part of the tissues.

On 11th July, 1888, there was issued from the Imperial Press at Berlin a pamphlet 62 pages long, entitled '*Die Krankheit Kaiser Friedrich des Dritten*', with an imposing list of authors on its cover: Professor von Bergmann (who was understood to be the editor), Professors Gerhardt, Waldeyer, Tobold, von Schrötter and several others. Neither Virchow nor, of course, Mackenzie was among them. Mackenzie was violently attacked in the pamphlet regarding his optimism that led to the postponement of an operation. Gerhardt prided himself on his diagnosis – 'In no other case,' he said, 'was the disease recognized so early.' And von Bergmann boasted about his seven successful cases of laryngo-fissure, but did not mention the fact that in no case was the operation for cancer. Gerhardt went so far as to put on record here his wild accusation that Mackenzie had damaged the *right* vocal cord when taking his first biopsy, and suggested, indeed, that he had deliberately taken the specimen from the healthy vocal cord!

It was only after the appearance of this malicious and libellous pamphlet that Mackenzie wrote his own ill-advised and vehement rejoinder, *The Fatal Illness of Frederick the Noble*, which was published on 15th October, 1888. It was unfavourably reviewed by nearly all the newspapers and particularly by the medical journals, for Mackenzie's meticulous descriptions of sickroom scenes and of operations was deemed most unethical, as were his violent attacks on Professor von Bergmann and Professor Gerhardt – he wrote about von Bergmann, the surgeon, after all, who was most responsible for developing asepsis from Lister's antisepsis, as 'not always paying regard to personal cleanliness', and Gerdhardt, a Royal Professor at Berlin University, as 'incompetent, indiscreet, and obstructive'.

On 23rd November 1888, Mackenzie, having been given a friendly hint, resigned his Membership of the Royal College of Physicians, to avoid any discussions there. On 10th January 1889, the behaviour of Mackenzie was discussed and censured at a meeting of the Council of the Royal College of Surgeons. And in January 1889, a memorial was sent to Professor von Bergmann from the British Medical Association, signed by 186 of its leading members, headed by Lord Lister, expressing the regrets of the Association for the publication in its *Journal* of two facsimiles of notes from the Emperor Frederick which reflected upon von Bergmann's treatment of him.

Mackenzie, who was a life-long asthmatic, returned from Berlin in ill-health. His exuberant energy had disappeared, although now and then a flicker of his old bright confidence would reappear, especially after a holiday abroad. He had a severe attack of influenza in 1890 and again in November 1891; pneumonia developed as a complication of the influenza and on 3rd February 1892, he died at the age of 54.

VII

The vacillations of Mackenzie's diagnosis and treatment of the case of the Emperor Frederick are to us nowadays almost incredible in a man of his experience and professional standing. In May 1887, he considered that the laryngeal condition was not cancer; in November 1887, he told the Crown Prince that the disease 'looked very

much like cancer but that it was impossible to be certain'; a few days
later he agreed with his colleagues that the disease was cancer – and
yet assented to large doses of potassium iodide being given in case it
was not; on 18th February 1888, he described the disease as chronic
interstitial inflammation of the larynx; at the beginning of March
he accepted the microscopic evidence in favour of cancer (such as it
was – it does not sound very conclusive) produced by Waldeyer,
and signed a joint statement with his colleagues to that effect; on
24th March he thought that the disease might after all possibly be
limited to perichondritis; in April he told Queen Victoria that the
Emperor would not live above a few weeks; in May he was expressing hopes about 'permanent improvement'; and on 31st May he told
the Empress Frederick that the Emperor 'might recover, though it
was not probable'; on 6th June, only nine days before the Emperor's
death, he discontinued daily bulletins as no longer necessary; and
then on 16th June he signed a report that the disease from which the
Emperor had died was cancer.

Mackenzie kept changing his mind because of his essentially
optimistic nature and because of the different signs and symptoms
presented by the patient. He was influenced also by the varying
opinions of his numerous German colleagues, and by his agreeable
habit of trying to please everybody. He rightly kept emphasizing
the decisive part played in regard to diagnosis by the pathological
opinions of Professor Virchow – a share in the responsibility which
Virchow never accepted. Only a fortnight before the death of the
Emperor Virchow said that 'the existence of a new malignant growth
was unproved and the disease was localized.' Politics also came into
it, for Virchow was a politician as well as a pathologist and a
strenuous opponent of Bismarck in the German Parliament.

Lionel Colledge, a laryngologist with an unusually wide experience of cancer of the larynx, stated in 1936 that he believed that
the reason why Mackenzie failed to recognize the nature of the
disease and to obtain specimens of tissue from which a correct
diagnosis could have been made was that the cancer was sub-

glottic, a type of cancer of the larynx with which, he suggested, Mackenzie was unfamiliar. In answer to this, it should be pointed out that Mackenzie in his textbook does say that in two out of his 53 cases of laryngeal cancer 'the left vocal cord and sub-glottic region were affected.' Colledge goes on to point out, however, that Mackenzie's illustration (page 59) shows a tumour far back in the larynx over the vocal process where the upper extension of a sub-glottic cancer might show itself, 'and where an epithelioma of the vocal cord would be most unlikely to make its first appearance.'

'If von Bergmann,' continues Colledge, 'had performed the operation which he proposed in May, 1887, he would have found the growth far more extensive than he expected ... It is quite likely that had the larynx been opened as he intended in May, 1887, it would have been found, when the interior was exposed to full view, that the extent of the growth already called for a total extirpation of the larynx.'

One must remember the date – 1887–88, before bacteriological examination of the sputum for tubercle bacilli, before X-ray examination of the lungs, before the Wassermann and Kahn blood tests for syphilis were known, when the microscopic examination of many pathological conditions was far from precise. The fact that at San Remo four of the most experienced laryngologists in Europe agreed to treat the laryngeal condition of the German Crown Prince with large doses of potassium iodide only a day or two before they publicly stated that he was suffering from cancer of the larynx, shows how speculative must have been the diagnosis of many tumours of the larynx at this period.

The first larynx ever removed by Billroth of Vienna, the pioneer of laryngectomy, in 1873, was found to be tuberculous, not cancer, after removal. In the 1937 edition of his textbook Sir St Clair Thomson records 'an instructive case', which he had reported at the old London Laryngological Society in 1899: 'The diagnosis of malignant disease was made by several experts after the administration of potassium iodide, where a laryngectomy was initiated and abandoned as hopeless owing to the involvement of glands, and where the patient made a spontaneous recovery after tracheotomy.'

Re-reading the descriptions of the perichondritis and the sloughing cartilages of the larynx (the large slough from the larynx expectorated on 17th January was 2 inches long and $\frac{1}{2}$ inch wide), it sounds – to me at least – much more like syphilis of the larynx than cancer, and the ulcers did heal under the administration of potassium iodide, which is used to treat 'tertiary' or late syphilis. The first small tumour of the left vocal cord looks in the drawing (which was accepted by all as accurate) more like a non-malignant granuloma than a cancer, possibly caused by the thirteen applications of the galvano-cautery. Professor R. A. Willis of Leeds, a well-known pathologist, writes (in 1953): 'Papillomas in adults; after repeated recurrences some of these show invasive carcinoma.' And Dr J. E. Ash, formerly director of the U.S. Army Institute of Pathology, writes: 'Adult papilloma of the larynx frequently results in squamous cell carcinoma.' The microscopic part of the post-mortem examination, carried out by Virchow some time later, does mention cell-nests (or rather, 'nest-cells') and it is possible – though not proven – that a cancer of the larynx supervened upon a syphilitic infection.

Did Morell Mackenzie – after all, he was one of the leading laryngologists in the world – know or suspect this? My own opinion is that he did, and that he concealed his knowledge in loyalty to the Emperor Frederick: how could he possibly have made it public at the time? Although this is not absolute proof, I was told by the late Dr Richard King Pierce, one of Mackenzie's most intimate friends, that Mackenzie confided in him, as a secret, after the death of the Emperor Frederick, that his patient had had syphilis of the larynx. Mark Hovell, a man of the highest integrity, never, I must admit, suggested the possibility to me. Was it in the character of 'Frederick the Noble' ever to have contracted syphilis? Well, he was a soldier, and had travelled unaccompanied in some odd parts of the world – there was gossip about him and a Spanish dancer in Egypt in 1869.

And it is well known that two Victorian statesmen of good reputation died from 'general paralysis', then considered an interesting but obscure neurological disease, but now known to be syphilitic in origin.

Morell Mackenzie was able, ambitious, conceited, eager for honours and publicity, jealous, self-assertive, sometimes bad-tempered, often kind-hearted, loyal to his friends, with the 'cleverest hands in the world'. The case of the Emperor Frederick made Mackenzie's name known – not always favourably – throughout the world, but it also served to put the new specialty of laryngology on the map.

The ardent spirit of Mackenzie still lives: his elder daughter became Mrs Theodore McKenna (sister-in-law of the Liberal statesman in Asquith's Cabinet), her son was Terence Morell McKenna of Christie's, and his daughter, Miss Virginia McKenna, is the well-known British film actress.

REFERENCES

SIR MORELL MACKENZIE. *Diseases of the Throat and Nose,* 2 vols. Churchill, London. Vol. I, 1880; Vol. II, 1884.

idem. Frederick the Noble, Sampson Low, London 1888.

E. VON BERGMANN, GERHARDT AND OTHERS. *Die Krankheit Kaiser Friedrich des Dritten,* Berlin 1888.

British Medical Journal: 1888, Vol. *ii,* pages 835, 887, 1412.

The Times: September–December 1887, January–June, 1888.

JEAN DE BONNEFON. *Drame Impérial,* E. Dentu, Paris 1888.

PRINCE OTTO VON BISMARCK. *Reflections and Reminiscences,* 2 vols. Trans. by A. J. Butler, Smith Elder, London 1898.

SIR FREDERICK PONSONBY. *Letters of the Empress Frederick,* Macmillan, London 1928.

G. E. BUCKLE (Editor). *Letters of Queen Victoria.* Third Series, Vol. I. John Murray, London 1930.

LIONEL COLLEDGE. *The laryngeal disease of the Emperor Frederick.* Journal of Laryngology and Otology, Vol. 51, p. 31. 1936.

SIR ST. CLAIR THOMSON and V. E. NEGUS. *Diseases of the Nose and Throat,* Cassell, London 1937.

R. SCOTT STEVENSON. *Morell Mackenzie*, Heinemann (Medical Books), London 1946.

J. E. ASH. Chapter 24 in W. A. D. ANDERSON'S *Pathology*, H. Kimpton, London 1953.

R. A. WILLIS. *Pathology of Tumours*, 2nd edition. Butterworth, London 1953.

JÜRGEN THORWALD. *The Triumph of Surgery*, p. 205. Thames & Hudson, London 1960.

CHAPTER VI

THE DELICATE HEALTH OF CHARLES DARWIN

IT was Charles Darwin more than any other individual who changed the whole course of Victorian thought, abolished old ideas about the immutability of species, and gave a new direction to many different fields of science. He had an extraordinary power of collecting and marshalling facts, but he often said that 'no one could be a good observer unless he was an active theorizer'.

His autobiography is full of complaints about his ill-health. He considered that he had done a good day's work when he had spent two or three hours writing while lying on a sofa, and sometimes he could do no work at all for months at a time. He lived, however, to the ripe age of 74, and his ill-health appears to have been entirely functional, due to an inherited psychological instability. He used it, in fact, as a protection from the world and especially from 'the distractions of society and amusement'. Having accumulated his mass of facts in earlier life, his ill-health and sleepless nights gave him the time to think and to concentrate his thoughts. Without it there would probably have been no *Origin of Species* nor *Descent of Man*.

Charles Darwin's father was a successful doctor in Shrewsbury. He made a large fortune from the practice of his profession, as could be done in those days, so that his son Charles never had to worry about earning his living. His grandfather was the once-famous Erasmus Darwin, poet and philosopher, a physician at Lichfield and then at Derby, author of the poem *The Botanic Garden* and of *Zoonomia*, which anticipated the theories of Lamarck. The story is that Erasmus Darwin took his son, when he qualified as a doctor, to Shrewsbury in 1787 and left him £20 with which to start medical practice; but it rather spoils the story to know that he also got £1,000 under his mother's settlement and £400 from an aunt.

In his autobiography Charles Darwin said that his father was 'the largest man that he ever saw': he was 6 feet 2 inches in height, with broad shoulders, and weighed 24 stones. His chief mental characteristics were his powers of observation and his sympathy. 'I suppose,' wrote Charles Darwin, 'that it was his sympathy that gave him unbounded power of winning confidence, and as a consequence made him highly successful as a physician.'

Dr Douglas Hubble has suggested that 'Charles Darwin's illness arose from the suppression and non-recognition of a painful emotion. Such an emotion is always compounded of fear, guilt or hate, and in Charles Darwin this emotion arose from his relationship with his father'. It would seem from the available evidence, however, that Charles got on well enough with his father, who cheerfully allowed him to give up the study of medicine at Edinburgh for not very arduous studies, with a country rectory in view, at Cambridge; and even at boarding-school, where he had 'the great advantage of living the life of a true schoolboy', the young Charles was happy that his home was only a mile away and he was able to 'keep up home affections and interests'.

The reason for Charles Darwin's ill-health is more likely to be found in his heredity: his grandmother was a hysteric who took to drink, and her father had been a chronic drunkard; his grandfather Erasmus and his uncle Charles both stammered badly; his father's enormous corpulence pointed to some endocrine instability; his uncle Erasmus committed suicide at the age of 40 'in a state of incipient insanity'; his brother Erasmus, who lived to the age of 77, was a chronic (probably neurotic) invalid; his mother had died when he was only eight years old.

II

Charles Darwin was sent to Shrewsbury School, under Dr Butler, in 1818, and remained there for seven years. But nothing could have been worse for the development of Darwin's mind than this school, 'as it was strictly classical, nothing else being taught, except a little ancient geography and history. The school as a means of education to me', he wrote in his autobiography, 'was simply a blank'.

As Charles was doing no good at school, his father took him away at a rather earlier age than usual, and sent him to Edinburgh University along with his brother, who was already there. The intention was to make a doctor of him, and Edinburgh was at that time the leading medical school, for the London hospitals, where students 'walked the wards', did little or no teaching except of anatomy. Edinburgh was, however, then and for many years afterwards dedicated to the idea that any subject could be taught by a hundred lectures, and Darwin found this boring. 'The instruction at Edinburgh,' he wrote in his autobiography, 'was altogether by lectures and these were intolerably dull, with the exception of those on chemistry by Hope; but to my mind there are no advantages and many disadvantages in lectures compared with reading. Dr Duncan's lectures on materia medica at 8 o'clock on a winter's morning are something fearful to remember. Dr Monro made his lectures on human anatomy as dull as he was himself, and the subject disgusted me. It has proved one of the greatest evils in my life that I was not urged to practise dissection, for I should soon have got over my disgust; and the practice would have been invaluable for all my future work. This has been an irremediable evil, as well as my incapacity to draw. I also attended regularly the clinical wards in the Hospital. Some of the cases distressed me a good deal, and I still have vivid pictures before me of some of them; but I was not so foolish as to allow this to lessen my attendance . . .

'I also attended on two occasions the operating theatre in the hospital at Edinburgh, and saw two very bad operations, one on a child, but I rushed away before they were completed. Nor did I ever attend again, for hardly any inducement would have been strong enough to make me do so; this being long before the blessed days of chloroform. The two cases fairly haunted me for many a long year.'

In his second year at Edinburgh Charles Darwin's elder brother had left, and he became acquainted with several young men who were fond of the natural sciences. One or two of them were interested particularly in marine zoology, and Darwin often accompanied them to collect animals in the tidal pools, which he dissected as well as he could. But from not having had any regular practice in dissection and possessing only 'a wretched microscope', his attempts were very poor. Nevertheless he made one interesting if minor discovery, and in 1826 read a short paper before the Plinian Society, which used to meet in an underground room in the University to read and discuss papers on natural science.

Having spent two 'sessions' at Edinburgh, his father realized that Darwin did not like the idea of being a doctor, so he suggested that he should become a clergyman and he was entered at Christ's College, Cambridge. 'By answering well the examination questions in Paley,' wrote Darwin in his autobiography, 'by doing Euclid well, and by not failing miserably in Classics, I gained a good place among the *oi polloi*, or crowd of men who do not go in for honours.' He was, in fact, tenth in the list, in 1831.

On the whole, however, Charles Darwin thought that his time at Cambridge was wasted. 'From my passion for shooting and for hunting and when this failed, for riding across country I got into a sporting set, including some dissipated low-minded young men. We used often to dine together in the evening, though these dinners often included men of a higher stamp, and we sometimes drank too much, with jolly singing and playing at cards afterwards.'

He became interested in art, and frequently went to the Fitz-william Museum, admiring particularly the paintings of Sebastian del Piombo; and he also got into a musical set, timed his walks so as to hear on week-days the anthem in King's College Chapel, and even sometimes hired the chorister boys to sing in his rooms.

But no pursuit at Cambridge was followed with so much eagerness or gave Charles Darwin so much pleasure as the collecting of beetles. 'No poet,' he wrote, 'ever felt more delight in seeing his first poem published than I did at seeing in Stephen's *Illustrations of British Insects* the magic words "captured by C. Darwin, Esq."' During his last year at Cambridge he read Humboldt's *Personal Narrative* of his travels and Sir J. Hershel's *Introduction of Natural Philosophy*, which influenced him more than any other books. His summer vacations were given up to collecting beetles, reading, and short tours. In the autumn his whole time was devoted to shooting. 'Upon the whole,' wrote Darwin in his autobiography, 'the three years which I spent at Cambridge were the most joyful in my happy life; for I was then in excellent health, and almost always in high spirits.'

III

On returning in 1831 from a short geological tour in North Wales, Charles Darwin found a letter from his friend Henslow, the botanist, informing him that Captain Fitz-Roy, hydrographer and meteorologist, 'was willing to give up part of his cabin to any young man who would volunteer to go with him without pay as naturalist to the voyage of H.M.S. *Beagle*'. His father put forward various obvious objections, but his uncle, Josiah Wedgwood, thought it would be wise to accept the offer, persuaded his father, and 'all was soon arranged'. The voyage of the *Beagle*, a tiny 242-ton brig, which was to sail on a five-year voyage of surveying, was the most important event in Darwin's life and determined his whole career. 'I have always felt,' he wrote, 'that I owe to the voyage the first real training or education of my mind.'

On the voyage Darwin read Sir Charles Lyell's *Principles of Geology*, which had an important influence by showing him the vast changes brought about by natural processes. 'On first examining a new district,' wrote Darwin, 'nothing can appear more hopeless than the chaos of rocks; but by recording the stratification and nature of the rocks and fossils at many points, always reasoning and predicting what will be found elsewhere, light soon becomes to dawn on the district, and the structure of the whole becomes more or less intelligible.'

Another of Darwin's occupations was collecting animals of all classes, briefly describing and roughly dissecting many of the marine ones. But, as he wrote, 'the various special studies were, however, of no importance compared with the habit of energetic industry and of concentrated attention to whatever I was engaged in, which I then acquired'.

While waiting at Plymouth for two months for the *Beagle* to sail, Charles Darwin had his first experience of the psychosomatic disorders that were to trouble him in later years. 'I was out of spirits at the thought of leaving all my family and friends for so long a time, and the weather seemed to me inexpressibly gloomy. I was also troubled with palpitation and pain about the heart, and like many a young ignorant man, especially one with a smattering of medical knowledge, was convinced that I had heart disease. I did not consult my doctor, as I fully expected to hear the verdict that I was not fit for the voyage, and I was resolved to go at all hazards.'

The long voyage of the *Beagle* became the most famous of all voyages of scientific discovery. The first land that Darwin saw, St Jago in the Cape Verde Islands, was an incontrovertible demonstration of the new ideas in geology. 'The geology of St Jago is very striking,' he wrote, 'but simple: a stream of lava formerly flowed over the bed of the sea, formed of triturated recent shells and corals, which it has baked into a hard white rock. Since then the whole island has been upheaved. But the line of white rock revealed to me a new and important fact, namely, that there had been afterwards subsidence round the craters, which had since been in action, and had poured forth lava.' Lyell's *Principles of Geology*, which contradicted the theological, cataclysmic geology before it, taught

Darwin not only to think about geology, but to think. In his explorations of South America it was the geological aspects that excited him most. He discovered near Bahia the fossil bones of a giant sloth, but mingled with them were marine shells 'identical with what now exist'. The volcanic islands which he visited stimulated new ideas. The Galapagos Islands in particular interested him: each island had great numbers of species and varieties of animals peculiar to itself, but differed from each other according to the natural barriers between them. Could St Helena be classed, however remotely, either with Africa or South America? 'It occurred to me,' he wrote, 'that possibly part of the peculiarity of the St Helena and Galapagos floras may be attributed to a great part of these floras being mountain floras.' His work on coral reefs and atolls meant much hard work, as he had to read every work on the islands of the Pacific and consult many charts. No other work of his was begun in so deductive a spirit as this, for the whole theory was thought out on the west coast of South America, before he had ever seen a true coral reef.

The *Beagle* visited Tahiti, New Zealand, Australia, Tasmania, the Maldives, Mauritius, Ascension, Brazil and the Azores. Towards the end of the voyage Darwin received a letter from his sisters in which they told him that Sedgwick had called on his father and said 'that Charles Darwin would take a place among the leading scientific men'. He could not at the time understand why this should have been predicted, but learned later that Henslow had read some of his letters before the Philosophical Society of Cambridge, and had had them printed for private distribution.

IV

Charles Darwin returned to England on 2nd October 1836, stayed for a time in Cambridge, and then took lodgings in Great Marlborough Street in London, where he remained for two years, until he was married. During that time he became one of the honorary secretaries of the Geological Society, finished his *Journal*, read

F

several papers before the Geological Society, prepared the manuscript for his *Geological Observations*, and arranged for the publication of his *Zoology of the Voyage of the 'Beagle'*. In July, 1837, he opened his first notebook for facts in relation to the origin of species, about which he had long reflected, and never ceased working on it for the next twenty years.

About this time he took much delight in the poetry of Wordsworth and Coleridge, 'and can boast that I read the *Excursion* twice through'. Formerly Milton's *Paradise Lost* had been his chief favourite, and in his excursions during the voyage of the *Beagle* when he could take only a single small volume, he always chose Milton. Later on, as his ill-health depressed him, he found that he lost completely his pleasure in poetry.

Charles Darwin married his cousin, Emma Wedgwood, on 29th January 1839. It was probably inevitable, as the families had been interlinked for generations. She was aged 30, a year older than Charles, had spent a year in Geneva, and returned to London to the usual round of the society to which she belonged, of dances, concerts, and theatres. She had no interest in geology or biology, but Charles was fortunately also interested in music and especially the piano, in which Emma was talented. She wrote to her aunt, 'he is the most open, transparent man I ever saw, and every word expresses his real thoughts. He is particularly affectionate and very nice to his brothers and sisters, and perfectly sweet tempered'.

'My last two days in London,' he wrote, 'when I wanted to have most leisure, were rendered very uncomfortable by a bad headache, which continued two days and two nights, so that I doubted whether it ever meant to go and allow me to be married.' They took a house in Upper Gower Street, in Bloomsbury, and settled down there for the next four years. 'During the early part of our life in London,' wrote Darwin, 'I was strong enough to go into general society, and saw a good deal of several scientific men and other more or less distinguished men.' But during the time they lived in London, Darwin confessed that he did less scientific work than during any other equal length of time in his life. This was 'owing to frequently recurring unwellness, and to one long and serious illness'.

After several fruitless searches in Surrey and elsewhere, Darwin and his wife found, at Down in Kent, and at moderate cost, an unpretentious, square brick house, with a drawing-room and dining-room that looked out on a broad expanse of lawn. It pleased them because of its 'extreme quietness and rusticity', yet it was only a quarter of a mile from the village of Down, ten miles from a railway station, and sixteen miles from London. Long afterwards, the house and grounds were presented to the Royal College of Surgeons by Sir Buckston Browne.

'Few persons,' wrote Darwin, 'can have lived a more retired life than we have done. Besides short visits to the houses of relations, and occasionally to the seaside or elsewhere, we have gone nowhere. During the first part of our residence we went a little into society, and received a few friends here; but my health almost always suffered from the excitement, violent shivering and vomiting attacks being thus brought on. I have therefore been compelled for many years to give up all dinner-parties; and this has been somewhat of a deprivation to me, as such parties always put me into high spirits. From the same cause I have been able to invite here very few scientific acquaintances. Whilst I was young and strong I was capable of very warm attachments, but of late years, though I still have very friendly feelings towards many persons, I have lost the power of becoming deeply attached to anyone, not even so deeply to my good and dear friends Hooker and Huxley, as I should formerly have been.'

From Down were published his various scientific writings, and in the summer of 1858 Alfred Russell Wallace, then in the Malay archipelago, sent him an essay, *On the Tendency of Varieties to depart indefinitely from the Original Type*, which contained exactly the same theory as his own. At the request of his friends Lyell, the geologist, and Hooker, the botanist, Darwin consented to an abstract of his manuscript being published at the same time as Wallace's essay, in the *Journal of the Proceedings of the Linnean Society*. Nevertheless, this joint production excited very little attention at the time.

In September, 1858, Darwin was persuaded by Lyell and Hooker to prepare a volume on the transmutation of species, 'but was often interrupted by ill-health, and short visits to Dr Lane's delightful hydropathic establishment at Moor Park'. It took thirteen months to write, was published in November 1859, under the title of *Origin of Species*, and was highly successful: the first edition of 1,250 copies was sold out on the day of publication, and a second edition of 3,000 copies soon afterwards; by 1876, when Darwin was writing his autobiography, 16,000 copies had been sold in England, and it was translated into almost every European language. One reason for the success of the book was its moderate size – when Darwin began to write it he contemplated a book four or five times as large.

V

Charles Darwin was fortunate in having T. H. Huxley as his advocate and expositor, for he himself was quite unfitted by temperament for the controversies which Huxley enjoyed. Huxley was a doctor, educated at Charing Cross Hospital, where he qualified in 1846. He was a brilliant student, winning a gold medal in anatomy and physiology at London University, and was appointed assistant surgeon to H.M.S. *Rattlesnake*, which had been ordered to survey the coasts and waters of north-eastern Australia and New Guinea, as the captain wanted someone 'who knew something of science'. Huxley was more interested in biology than in medical practice, and had been trained in the scientific method by Wharton Jones, lecturer on physiology at Charing Cross medical school. In the *Rattlesnake* Huxley worked with MacGillivray, who was naturalist to the expedition, and accumulated a mass of scientific observations; his memoir on the structure of the Medusae (jelly-fish) was published in the *Philosophical Transactions* of the Royal Society. The cruise of the *Rattlesnake* lasted for four years, but when he returned to

England, Huxley found that his scientific standing was well-recognized, and in 1851, before he was 26, he was elected F.R.S.

The *Rattlesnake* had spent several months at Sydney, where Huxley fell in love with the daughter of one of the leading merchants, but was not able to afford to marry her for eight more years. He was awarded the coveted Royal Medal of the Royal Society; yet he could obtain no suitable appointment, and kept going only by writing a textbook on comparative anatomy, contributing articles on scientific subjects to the monthly and quarterly reviews, and translating German scientific works.

Then his friend Forbes was appointed a professor at Edinburgh University, and Huxley found himself appointed in his stead a lecturer at the Government School of Mines in Jermyn Street, London, followed by other appointments under the Geological Survey and at St Thomas's Hospital medical school. Professor Forbes died soon after and Huxley might have succeeded him at Edinburgh, but preferred to take his chance in London. In 1855 he was able at last to marry and remained devoted to his wife for the next forty years. Darwin warned him, 'I hope your marriage will not make you idle; happiness, I fear, is not good for work.' Paleontology and administrative work now began to take up a great deal of his attention; he was Naturalist to the Geological Survey for over thirty years, and published a long series of papers dealing with fossil creatures.

In November 1859, Darwin published his *Origin of Species*, which gave a new direction to Huxley's activities. He had had many talks with Darwin ever since the famous joint communication with A. R. Wallace to the Linnean Society in 1858, but the effect of the book itself, with its detailed arguments and overwhelming array of evidence, was far greater than that of previous discussions. Huxley accepted Darwin's theory as a well-founded working hypothesis, calculated to explain problems otherwise inexplicable. 'My reflection,' wrote Huxley afterwards, 'when I first made myself master of the central idea of the *Origin* was, "How extremely stupid not to have thought of that!'"

The Origin of Species was sent for review in the ordinary way to one of the staff of *The Times*, who, knowing little about science, asked his friend Huxley to help him out with the review. Huxley seized the opportunity: 'Of course as a scientific review,' he wrote to his friend Hooker, the botanist, 'the thing is worth nothing, but I earnestly hope it may have made some of the educated mob, who derive their ideas from *The Times*, reflect. And whatever they do they *shall* respect Darwin.'

The famous Oxford Meeting in 1860 of the British Association for the Advancement of Science was an important milestone in the careers of both Huxley and Darwin. It was known that Bishop Wilberforce, 'Soapy Sam', as he was irreverently nicknamed, intended at it to 'smash Darwin'. It was only by chance that Huxley attended the meeting on the Saturday morning, when Dr Draper of New York read a paper for discussion on 'The intellectual development of Europe considered with reference to the views of Mr Darwin'. The long west room of the Museum was packed with 700 listeners who had come to hear Bishop Wilberforce's eloquence. Professor Henslow, the distinguished botanist, was in the chair of the Section, the Bishop was on his right, and Dr Draper beyond him. The clergy were massed in the middle of the room, behind them were a group of undergraduates, and the windows were packed with ladies in summer dresses, fluttering their handkerchiefs at the end of the Bishop's speech. Two or three other speakers in the discussion preceded him, and it was soon evident that he knew nothing of the subject at first hand – he had, in fact, been 'crammed' by his friend Sir Richard Owen, the anatomist, who had been staying with him at Cuddesdon. For half an hour the Bishop spoke 'with inimitable spirit, emptiness and unfairness'. In a light, scoffing tone, florid and fluent, he assured his audience that 'There was nothing in the idea of evolution; rock-pigeons were what rock-pigeons had always been. Then turning to his antagonist, Huxley, with a smiling insolence, he begged to know, was it through his grandfather or his grandmother that he claimed his descent from a monkey?'

Huxley murmured to Sir Benjamin Brodie, the veteran surgeon who was sitting next to him, 'The Lord hath delivered him into mine hands.' He rose up slowly and deliberately, a slight, tall figure, stern and pale, and explained that the suggestion was of descent through thousands of generations from a common ancestor, and then went on: 'But if this question is treated, not as a matter for the calm investigation of science, but as a matter of sentiment, and if I am asked whether I would choose to be descended from the poor animal of low intelligence and stooping gait, who grins and chatters as we pass, or from a man, endowed with great ability and a splendid position, who should use these gifts to discredit and crush humble seekers after truth, I hesitate what answer to make.'

The importance of the Oxford meeting, as Leonard Huxley wrote in his *Life* of his father, 'lay in the open resistance that was made to authority, at a moment when even a drawn battle was hardly less effectual than acknowledged victory. Instead of being crushed under ridicule, the new theories secured a hearing, all the wider, indeed, for the startling nature of their defence.'

VI

Darwin, with intervals of ill-health, kept on writing long articles for the scientific journals, and in 1868 published an important book, which had taken four years to write, *Variation of Animals and Plants under Domestication*. Then, in February, 1871, there was published his second great work, *The Descent of Man*, which sold 7,500 copies before the end of the year, and did not receive any abuse in the reviews. For three years Darwin had worked on this book, which grew interminably longer, until his daughter Henrietta sub-edited it down to a mere 688 pages.

Darwin concluded that man owed his supremacy not to any one characteristic but to many, his upright stance, the freedom and delicacy of his hands, the use of tools and language and, above all, to the mental capacity that made tools and language possible. He regarded mind as an adaptation to environment and a weapon in the struggle for survival. He insisted on the great gap between man and the higher mammals and did not agree (with A. R. Wallace) that the savage could have discovered fire or developed language with a brain little better than that of the ape; yet he insisted also that man differed from animals physically, mentally and morally not in kind but in degree. He also discussed fully the subject of sexual selection, which had always interested him, and explained that for the possession of a mate the males of a species not only fight each other physically, but compete in displays of plumage and ornamentation, in erotic dances and song, 'so that the principle of utility seems to give way to that of beauty'. Racial differentiation he explained by divergent masculine conceptions of female good looks – negroes were black and flat-nosed because their remote male ancestors preferred women with dark skins and flat noses. Similarly he considered that 'sexual selection made women more tender, affectionate and unselfish, and men more courageous, energetic and intelligent'.

Darwin's son wrote in the *Life and Letters* of his father: 'He bore his illness with such uncomplaining patience, that even his children can hardly, I believe, realize the extent of his habitual suffering. In their case the difficulty is heightened by the fact that, from the days of their earliest recollections, they saw him in constant ill-health . . . No one indeed, except my mother, knows the full amount of suffering he endured, or the full amount of his wonderful patience. For all the latter years of his life she never left him for a night; and her days were so planned that all his resting hours might be shared with her'.

Dr Douglas Hubble writes: 'A succession of doctors and a plenitude of treatment were necessary to protect him from the suspicion of shamming.' In February 1840, Darwin had written to his friend Lyell: 'Dr Holland thinks he has found out what is the matter with me, and now hopes he shall be able to set me going again. Is it not mortifying, it is now nine weeks since I have done a whole day's work, and not more than four half days.'

When orthodox medicine failed, Darwin had recourse to unorthodox practitioners. He went for some months to Malvern, where Dr Gully, lately returned from the German spas, was prescribing an elaborate water cure, which Darwin was able to carry out later at home, with the aid of his butler. 'My treatment is now, lamp five times per week, and shallow bath for five minutes afterwards; douche daily for five minutes and dripping sheet daily. The treatment is wonderfully tonic and I have had more better consecutive days this month than in any previous ones. I am allowed to work now two and a half hours daily, and I find it as much as I can do, for the cold-water cure together with three short walks, is curiously exhausting; and I am actually forced to go to bed completely tired. I steadily gain in weight, and eat immensely and am never oppressed with my food. I have lost the involuntary twitching of the muscles, and all the fainting feelings, etc. Black spots before the eyes, etc. Dr Gully thinks he shall quite cure me in six or nine months more.'

But the effect was transient only, and he changed to 'Dr Lane's beautiful water establishment at Moor Park, near Aldershot', which he visited regularly for several years. Then he tried Dr Brinton — 'One of the most cheery and skilful physicians of the day. He does not believe my heart or brain are primarily affected.' Two years later he was still ill and depressed, so he switched to Dr Bence-Jones, who 'half-starved me to death'. He also prescribed exercise on horseback, and Darwin rode 'Tommy, a cob, the easiest, the quietest in the world', until he fell with him on Keston Common, which upset his nerves.

In his last illness Darwin consulted the eminent Victorian physician Sir Andrew Clark, about whom his son wrote: 'It was not only for his generously rendered service that my father felt a debt of gratitude towards Sir Andrew Clark. He owed to his cheering personal influence an oft-repeated encouragement, which latterly added something real to his happiness.' His treatment was carried on by Dr Norman Moore of St Bartholomew's Hospital and Mr Allfrey of St Mary Cray. His son explained, 'Sir Andrew Clark himself was ever ready to devote himself to my father who, however, could not endure the thought of sending for him, knowing how severely his great practice taxed his strength.'

During the last ten years of his life the health of Charles Darwin had seemed to his family to improve: 'He suffered less distress and discomfort, and was able to work more steadily.' In 1880 he inherited a large fortune from his brother Erasmus, and a friend, Mr Anthony Rich, also informed him (though Darwin protested that he was already wealthy) that he intended to leave him nearly the whole of a large property. In December 1881, he had a heart attack when calling on a friend in London, and for the next two months he had frequent attacks of pain in the region of the heart. 'I am not the least afraid of death,' he said to his wife, 'remember what a good wife you have been to me.' He died on 10th April, 1882, from what was obviously a coronary thrombosis, aged 74, and was buried in Westminster Abbey.

REFERENCES

FRANCIS DARWIN. *Life and Letters of Charles Darwin*, 3 vols. John Murray, London 1887.

LEONARD HUXLEY. *Life and Letters of Thomas Henry Huxley*, 2 vols. Macmillan, London 1900.

DOUGLAS HUBBLE. *Charles Darwin and Psychotherapy*. The Lancet, Vol. *i*, p. 129. 1943.
idem: The Life of the Shawl. The Lancet, Vol. *ii*, p. 1351. 1953.

WALTER C. ALVAREZ. *The asthenia of Charles Darwin*, in *Nervousness, Indigestion and Pain*, Hoeber, New York 1947.

WILLIAM IRVINE. *Apes, Angels and Victorians*, Weidenfeld & Nicolson, London 1955.

LADY (NORA) BARLOW. *The Autobiography of Charles Darwin* (with original omissions restored). Collins, London 1958.

S. ADLER. *Darwin's Illness*. Nature. Vol. 184, p. 1102. 1959.

CHAPTER VII

THE ILL-HEALTH OF NAPOLEON III

THE reputation of Napoleon III has suffered from the vindictive supporters of the Third Republic – *Napoléon-le-petit* of Victor Hugo, *Badinguet* of Zola, the Crowned Carbonaro, and many other unkind epithets. Stockily built, with an unimpressive and unattractive appearance, Louis Napoleon nevertheless had an indefinable charm that captivated not only Queen Victoria but the less easily swayed Prince Albert, and he had an unswerving belief in his destiny. He invariably showed kindness and gratitude to old friends of less fortunate days, and his intimates and adherents were devoted to him.

He was industrious, a habit inculcated in early youth; he wrote well and persuasively though he spoke badly in public, and he was always a good listener. Paris as we know it, built by Baron Haussmann, with its boulevards, avenues and parks, was in essentials planned by Louis Napoleon, though its centre-piece, the Opera House which typifies the florid architecture of the period, was completed only after his death. Not only Gounod and Bizet, Offenbach and the can-can, but Flaubert, Renan, Daudet, Baudelaire, Verlaine and the brothers De Goncourt, Corot, Courbet, Manet, Pissarro and the Impressionists, were contemporary with the Second Empire of Napoleon III. He lived extravagantly, but he did more for France, for a longer period, and cared more for the welfare of its people, than his genius of an uncle ever did

The *coup d'état* that shocked England (though not France, accustomed to violent changes of government), and considered by

many a criminal adventure and the blackest spot on Louis Napoleon's career – for he broke his oath of loyalty to the Republic in
achieving it, not without bloodshed – was no more blood-stained
than the military *coup d'état* that put General de Gaulle into power,
and his dictatorship was benevolent when compared with those that
we have known. His foreign policy was founded on improvisation
rather than on any sound principles, except that he favoured an
English alliance and preferred large countries to a number of small
ones – including even the unification of Germany.

Probably war with Germany was inevitable, but had Napoleon
III won his battles in 1870 France would have acclaimed him as its
saviour and his liberalized Empire as its best and most enduring
form of government. He was a very sick man, however, with a
painful disease; his energy was impaired and his judgement dulled,
and he was pushed into a declaration of war by a restless and eager
Army 'ready to the last gaiter button', a chauvinistic Press, an
excited and over-sensitive Parliament, and a populace, drunk with
the Napoleonic legend, crying for *la gloire*.

II

Prince Louis Napoleon Bonaparte was the third son of Louis, King
of Holland, the younger brother of the Emperor Napoleon, and his
wife Hortense Beauharnais, daughter of the Empress Josephine and
step-daughter of Napoleon. The King of Holland was serious-
minded and morose, while Queen Hortense was young, gay and
musical, and although three sons were born of the marriage, it
culminated in unhappiness and separation. King Louis abdicated
from the throne of Holland and went to live in Florence with his
second son, for the eldest had died in childhood from 'croup', while
Queen Hortense went to Paris, where her youngest son, Louis
Napoleon, was born in 1808. After Waterloo and the restoration of
the Bourbons, Queen Hortense lived first in Augsburg, in Bavaria,
and then in 1820 settled down in Switzerland at the chateau of
Arenenberg, overlooking Lake Constance. The education of young

Prince Louis Napoleon was entrusted to an excellent scholar and tutor, Philippe Le Bas, son of the loyal Jacobin friend of Robespierre, and his sense of discipline and methodical methods of work during six years had the best possible influence upon his pupil.

In 1828 the young Prince went to Rome, where the Bonaparte family, with Madame Mère and Cardinal Fesch at its head, were settled. In 1830–31 he became involved, as a Carbonaro, in an anti-Papal revolt, and during the fighting his elder brother died at Forli – some say of measles (of which there was an epidemic), some say by a bullet, but the former is more probable. Louis Napoleon likewise went down with measles, and when he was convalescent his mother took him, by a series of stratagems, from Italy to Paris and on to London, where they made some useful friends. By the end of the year, however, they were back in Arenenberg, where he wrote his first political pamphlet, '*Rêveries politiques*'.

The death from tuberculosis of Napoleon's only son, the Duke of Reichstadt, in Vienna, made Louis Napoleon the heir to the Bonaparte succession, and he began to hitch his wagon to his star. His dreams were encouraged by a new acquaintance, a journalist named Jean Fialin, Vicomte de Persigny (some said self-styled), who became his most devoted follower and propagandist. Persigny persuaded him that support for the Bonapartist cause was wide-spread in France, and in October 1836 Louis Napoleon raised the standard of revolt against Louis-Philippe at Strasbourg, where an ardent Bonapartist, Colonel Vaudrey, was in command of the 4th regiment of artillery, the great Napoleon's old regiment. But the general commanding the garrison and the infantry remained loyal to the King, and the attempt was a failure. Instead of placing Louis Napoleon on trial the Government made light of the affair and merely deported him to the United States by way of Rio de Janeiro. In New York he received news of his mother's serious ill-health; a letter from her told him that the doctors had decided not to operate, but on the outside of the envelope Dr Conneau, her personal physician, had written, 'Venez, venez!' Louis Napoleon sailed at once and reached his mother's side two months later, but before her death.

Dr Henri Conneau was born in 1803, in Milan, when it was occupied by the Napoleonic army of the Consulate, the son of a French officer in the commissariat. He lived in Florence and while still young became private secretary to Louis Bonaparte, formerly King of Holland. He qualified as a doctor in Florence and practised for a time in Rome; but after the insurrection of 1831, in which some of his friends were involved, he went to Switzerland, where he became private medical attendant to Queen Hortense. On her death-bed, she confided her son Louis Napoleon to his care, and during all his misfortunes and successes Dr Conneau never left his side. He was with him at Ham, in the Tuileries and at Sedan, and stood beside him when he died at Chislehurst.

Louis Napoleon inherited a fortune from his mother, Queen Hortense, and with £5,000 a year at his disposal settled comfortably in Carlton Terrace, London, where he entertained well and chose his company carefully. He also installed a mistress, the beautiful blonde Miss Howard, in a little house in Berkeley Street. Miss Howard attracted attention by her magnificent appearance on horse-back and had had previous lovers, among them Kinglake the historian, who never forgave Louis Napoleon and took his revenge in a vicious caricature of him in his eight-volume *History of the Crimean War*.

In his political novel *Endymion*, Disraeli (who was a friend of his) pictures Louis Napoleon under the designation of Prince Florestan: 'The world thought that he had fitted up his fine house, and bought his fine horses, merely for the enjoyment of life. His purposes were very different. Though his acquaintances were limited they were not undistinguished, and he lived with them in intimacy ... It was an interesting and useful house for a young man, and especially a young politician, to frequent. The prince encouraged conversation, though himself inclined to taciturnity. When he did speak, his terse remarks and condensed views were striking, and were remembered.'

The Prince, however, also spent many hours studying at the British Museum, where his friend Panizzi (like himself, a former Carbonaro) was Keeper of the Printed Books. Addressed from Carlton Terrace, and dated July 1839, there was published in Paris and London his political manifesto, 50,000 words long, entitled *Des Idées Napoléoniennes*. The book was founded more upon the afterthoughts that Napoleon wrote and dictated at St Helena than upon his actions when he was at the height of his military career. 'What was his aim? Liberty. With his rule all the passions of revolution came to an end. Strong in the support of the people, he proceeded at once to abolish every unjust law, to heal every wound, to reward every merit, to exploit every achievement, and to secure the collaboration of all Frenchmen for a single end, the prosperity of France.' Nothing here of the despot who dotted his brothers and marshals on the thrones of Europe, of the ruthless conqueror of Marengo and Austerlitz, of Wagram and Borodino, of Dresden and Leipzig, or of the retreat from Moscow and the desperate raising of millions of conscripts, and nothing of Elba or of Waterloo.

'When the fate of arms had rendered Napoleon master of the greater part of the continent,' ended the *Idées*, 'he was anxious to apply his victories to the establishment of a European Confederation . . . To substitute, among the nations of Europe, the social state for the state of nature – such was the idea of the Emperor; all his political combinations tended to this immense result . . . The policy of the Emperor was to found a solid European association by resting his system on completed nationalities and satisfied general interests.'

'Napoleon fell solely because, his projects growing in proportion to the elements he had at his disposal, he sought, in ten years of Empire, to do the work of several centuries . . . It is a consolation for those who feel the blood of the great man flowing in their veins, to reflect upon the regrets which have accompanied his loss . . . Let us repeat in conclusion: the Napoleonic idea is not an idea of war, but a social, industrial, commercial idea – an idea of humanity.'

The slim volume, in green covers, stamped with the Imperial eagle, and published at half a franc, quickly went into four editions, was translated into English, German, Italian, Spanish, Portuguese, and Russian, and sold over 500,000 copies. Like Hitler's *Mein Kampf* nearly a hundred years later, his readers made the mistake of not taking the author's expressed intentions seriously.

The increasing unpopularity of King Louis-Philippe, which he hoped to assuage by promoting the Napoleonic legend, completing the Arc de Triomphe and bringing Napoleon's body back from St Helena to the church of the Invalides in Paris, encouraged another attempt at an uprising by Louis Napoleon. He chartered a small paddle-steamer, the *City of Edinburgh*, and sailed for Wimereux, near Boulogne, where Napoleon's *Grande Armée* had encamped in 1804 for three years, waiting for the invasion of England that never ensued. In the paddle-steamer were not only Louis Napoleon and a score of his friends in uniform, but three grooms, a crew of 19, 24 hampers of wine, besides beer, ginger-beer and soda-water, nine horses, two new carriages, and a live eagle. The landing proved a fiasco, for the soldiers of Boulogne repudiated the Prince, and he and his friends were taken prisoner. They were in due course brought for trial before the Court of Peers and sentenced to various terms of imprisonment, Napoleon being condemned for life in the fortress of Ham.

III

The ancient fortress of Ham, in the valley of the Somme, was built by the Count of St Pol in 1460; it is a damp place, in the midst of marshy country, and the mists are frequent. Napoleon had two white-washed rooms with brick floors, and the plain furniture supplied to officers in barracks. In his sitting-room he had book-shelves built, and planks against the wall made a dressing-table in his bedroom. He was accompanied by his friends and fellow-prisoners General Montholon (who had been with Napoleon at St Helena) and Dr Conneau, and by his valet Charles Thélin. The studious habits which the Prince had formed early in life stood him in good stead, and in after years he used to say, 'I took my honours at the University of Ham,' though he also complained bitterly of the rheumatism he contracted there, which made him lame.

In a few months time the Commandant, who used to play whist with him after dinner, allowed the Prince to correspond freely and to receive books (chiefly through his childhood companion, Madame Hortense Cornu) and visitors (including Alexandrine-Eléonore Vergeot, a local cobbler's daughter, by whom he had two sons – in after years they were to become Counts of the Second Empire). More surprisingly, no impediment was placed by the Government in the way of his many communications and articles in Opposition newspapers, especially the Republican *Progrès du Pas-de-Calais*. He spent three years writing an historical book on *The Past and Future of Artillery*; he also wrote a pamphlet on *The Extinction of Pauperism* (mainly by settling the unemployed on the waste lands of France), which was well received by working-class leaders; *Historical Fragments, 1688–1830*, refuting Guizot's comparison of the revolutions in England and in France; and a well-informed study of *The Beet-sugar Question*.

He became interested in the project of connecting the Atlantic and Pacific Oceans by a ship canal across Nicaragua, was visited by the Nicaraguan Minister and was petitioned by a 'great number of the principal inhabitants' of Nicaragua to undertake the enterprise. Years later he was to encourage de Lesseps to construct the Suez Canal.

Thus did Louis Napoleon pass nearly six years in his medieval prison, with massive stone walls, a moat, a drawbridge and a high watch-tower, guarded by 400 armed soldiers, sentries posted at every gateway. Escape seemed impossible – yet it was achieved in a simple, clever and lucky manner. Repairs were being carried out in the prison and workmen were passing in and out. Louis Napoleon's

G

valet procured sabots and a workman's blouse for him, he cut off his moustache, and took a plank upon his shoulder. When the workmen came in at six o'clock in the morning the valet offered them drinks, and Dr Conneau conversed with the guards. Screening his face with the plank Louis Napoleon walked out of his room and across the courtyard; the officer of the guard was reading a letter and did not notice him, and he found himself outside the fortress. Thélin, the valet, had the evening before engaged a cab to go to St Quentin, and picked up the Prince on the road; they arrived at Valenciennes, took a train to Brussels, and soon crossed to London.

Meanwhile Dr Conneau sent word to the Commandant that the Prince was unwell, made noxious smells in his room with the aid of some chemicals, and fixed up a dummy in his bed. When eventually the Commandant insisted that evening on seeing the Prince it was many hours too late. Dr Conneau was handcuffed and taken to Péronne, where he was sentenced to three months' imprisonment 'amid strong marks of public sympathy'. When he reached London, the Prince bought a medical practice for him for £900, though he was not destined to practise there for long.

IV

In the year 1848 a wave of unrest swept across Europe, though only a few ripples reached the shores of England, for the Reform Bill of 1832 and the repeal of the Corn Laws in 1846 had allayed popular feeling. But in Paris in February the mob, aided by a discontented National Guard, pulled down an unpopular government, and Louis-Philippe, taking fright – he was over 70 – escaped across the Channel to England. The republican provisional government proclaimed universal suffrage, increasing the electorate over thirty-fold to nine millions, mainly peasants, who were influenced by their priests. Among the candidates for Parliament was Louis Napoleon, who was elected, but he realized that feeling was still against him and wisely then withdrew.

France had not yet experienced the industrial revolution, and the resultant assembly was more conservative than had been anticipated, so that the leaders of the Parisian mob – not yet called socialists or communists – felt frustrated, and in June, 1848, a bitter revolt broke out in Paris. The mob fought behind street barricades, but the Army under General Cavaignac, reinforced by provincial detachments of the National Guard, ruthlessly shot them down.

At supplementary elections to Parliament in September Louis Napoleon was returned by five different constituencies, including Paris. The assembly could not resist this expression of popular feeling, and Napoleon took his seat in Parliament. His first speech was on an unexpected occasion and impromptu, and he made a poor appearance – Thiers rashly called him 'a *crétin* whom we can manage'. The leaders of the assembly did not worry, therefore, when he became a candidate for the Presidency of the Republic. But his chief opponent was General Cavaignac, who was unforgiven for his repressive measures in June, and Louis Napoleon was elected by 5,434,226 votes to 1,448,107, the support of the other three political candidates being negligible. During the next two or three years he made himself known throughout the country by making propagandist tours, he showed political strength by dismissing the ministry of Barrot and himself sitting at the head of meetings of the new ministry, and he replaced the republican General Changarnier, who commanded the troops in Paris, by a Bonapartist supporter from Algeria, General St Arnaud. The constitution did not allow the President to have a second term of office, so the group of devoted friends and adherents around Napoleon determined to out-manœuvre Parliament. The chief organizer was the brilliant and reckless Morny, his younger half-brother (an illegitimate son of Queen Hortense), and the other conspirators included his old friend Persigny, de Maupas, an able and unscrupulous prefect from Toulouse, who became Chief of Police, and General St Arnaud.

The date chosen was 2nd December 1851, the anniversary of Austerlitz, and during the previous night 50,000 troops under

General St Arnaud occupied the chief strategic points of Paris, including newspaper and printing works and the Palais Bourbon; church towers were guarded, and drums broken at the town halls of the various *arrondissements*. Sixteen members of Parliament and seventy other well-known opponents were arrested in their own homes; and when 300 other members of Parliament found themselves excluded from the Palais Bourbon they met at the town hall of the 10th *arrondissement*, where in turn they were arrested.

Next morning Louis Napoleon rode out from the Elysée Palace with a group of generals, including the one surviving brother of the Emperor Napoleon, Jerome, ex-King of Westphalia. There was no enthusiasm among the crowds, and within a day or two there was even some resistance in the streets and barricades were thrown up, but it was crushed by the troops in a few hours. Eight of Napoleon's leading opponents were sent to the fortress of Ham, many Parisians who had taken part in the fighting were condemned to death by court-martial, and there were 27,000 arrests by special tribunals throughout the country, of whom over 9,500 were transported to Algeria, 239 to Cayenne, and 1,500 exiled from France, mainly because of their left-wing political opinions. Napoleon realized at once that this was a mistake and pardoned some 4,000 of them, but the harm had been done and was not forgotten.

A plebiscite was held on 10th December, with eight million voters, of whom seven and a half million supported Napoleon, 'delegating to him the powers to establish a constitution'. The President was given authority to appoint all officials, from top to bottom, including the Ministers, the Senate, and the High Court of Justice, as well as the prefects and sub-prefects of every city and district. The times were fortunate for Louis Napoleon, for in France as elsewhere in Europe trade was beginning to boom: new railways and steamships were being built, factories and dwelling-houses were going up everywhere, new banks were founded, the bank rate was reduced and shares rose in value. No wonder that when, after a triumphant tour of the provinces in the autumn of 1852, another plebiscite was held on the proclamation of the Empire, it was approved by 7,800,000 votes in favour and only 250,000 against.

One of the first actions of the new Emperor (by a decree dated 31st December 1852) was to appoint his salaried medical household of twenty physicians and surgeons, with the faithful Dr Conneau as 'First Physician and Chief of the Health Service'.

V

An Emperor requires an heir to carry on his dynasty, and Napoleon III, after two or three ill-received soundings of the royal families in Europe, fell in love with a beautiful Spanish aristocrat, Eugenia de Montijo, aged 26. Strictly speaking, she could be called an adventuress – as, indeed, Napoleon III was an adventurer – but, though impoverished, she was well-behaved and mixed in the best circles in Madrid as well as in Paris and her sister had married the Duke of Alba. It was in the drawing-room of his cousin Princess Mathilde that Louis Napoleon met her, and she and her mother were invited to Fontainebleau and, for the hunting season, to Compiègne. Like Miss Howard (who had accompanied Napoleon to Paris), Eugenia looked her best on horseback, and Napoleon III quickly capitulated, against the advice of his friends.

On 30th January, 1853, they were married with the greatest pomp in Notre Dame, and the Empress Eugénie made him a good and courageous wife to the end of his days, even when she was inclined to meddle not very intelligently in politics. An heir, the Prince Imperial, was born on 16th March 1856. The childbirth was almost disastrous – at one stage the Emperor was asked to choose which life should be saved and insisted that it must be his wife's – and thereafter it is said that marital relations ceased, though Napoleon III had been strictly faithful for only six months after the marriage.

The Crimean War, which broke out in March 1854, helped Napoleon III to consolidate the alliance with England and enhance his prestige in Europe. It is often forgotten that it was only after the arrival in the Crimea, when reinforcements were urgent, of 15,000 Sardinian troops from Italy that Sebastopol fell. But Cavour and King Victor Emmanuel II did not forget, and they were convinced that only the military intervention of France could bring about the liberation of Italy from Austria and the temporal power of the Pope. Dr Conneau, who spoke Italian as a native, acted as a confidential agent between Napoleon III and Cavour, Austria was persuaded into the position of being the aggressor, and in April 1859, France declared war on Austria in support of Sardinia. At the confused victories of Magenta and Solferino the casualties were heavy, and as a result of his experiences on these battlefields Napoleon III promoted the Geneva Convention of 1864 that inaugurated the International Red Cross Society. An armistice in July, 1859, was welcomed on both sides, especially as Prussia was beginning to mobilize an army on the Rhine. France was rewarded for her help by the cession of Nice and Savoy.

Napoleon III's enlightened colonial policy did not conflict with Britain's, and included the development of Algeria and French West Africa, the occupation of New Caledonia and Tahiti, the colonization of Madagascar and French Somaliland. Then in 1861 France, Spain and Britain intervened in Mexico to protect the interests of foreign bond-holders, whose debts had been repudiated by an anti-clerical government. Differences of opinion arose, and Spain and Britain left France to carry on the dispute alone. Unfortunately a French army was defeated with heavy losses by the Mexican rebels, so that national honour had to be avenged. In addition, Mexico was Catholic and said to be monarchical and an assembly of notables had invited the Archduke Maximilian of Austria (younger brother of the Emperor Francis Joseph) to become its Emperor. With the aid of an army of over 30,000 French soldiers under General Bazaine, Maximilian and his wife Carlotta (daughter of King Leopold of Belgium) were put on the throne of Mexico, while the Civil War was distracting the attention of the United States.

But with the end of the Civil War in 1865 the United States was no longer indifferent, France began to experience difficulties in Europe, Maximilian was abandoned and shot by Mexican rebels and his wife went insane. While France was wasting its strength in this futile war in Mexico, Bismarck was quietly uniting Germany.

VI

In May 1856, when Napoleon III was aged 48 and in poor health, tired from the Peace Congress that ended the Crimean War, Dr Conneau called Sir William Fergusson from London in consultation, rather than a French surgeon, in case of an indiscreet disclosure. Fergusson, a Scotsman and a brilliant graduate of Edinburgh, was appointed professor of surgery at King's College Hospital, London, at the age of 32, and had become the leading surgeon in London. His attitude was conservative, in a day of ruthless amputations, and he said that it was 'a grand thing when even the tip of a thumb could be saved'. He devised his own lithotrite for crushing stone in the bladder, although he excelled in lithotomy, and he was the most dexterous practical surgeon of his time.

His very thorough examination of Napoleon III revealed a wide range of ailments, aggravated by constant hours at his desk and lack of exercise – neuralgia, sciatica, dyspepsia, loss of appetite, insomnia, irritability, and loss of sexual potency. Fergusson put his patient on a strict diet, cut down the large number of cigarettes that he was accustomed to smoke, and made other wise recommendations.

The persistent kidney and bladder ailments, from which the Emperor Napoleon III eventually died, date from 1861. In that year, during a stay at Vichy, he was catheterized by Dr Felix Guyon, professor of genito-urinary surgery in the Paris faculty of medicine, a leading authority on diseases of the prostate and urinary tract. Dr Guyon used a fine-calibre catheter and then passed a sound to relieve the symptoms caused by a post-gonorrhoeal stricture. For the Emperor had not only found the fair sex irresistable ever since his youth at Arenenberg, but he was rash and unselective in his pursuit of sexual pleasure. In 1864 he had a notorious liaison with a vulgar cocotte named Marguerite Bellanger, whom all Paris called 'Margot la Rigoleuse'. She had become pregnant by her Imperial protector, who lodged her in a villa close to the palace at St Cloud. 'This new fatherhood on the part of the Emperor,' wrote Octave Aubry, 'irritated Eugénie to the last extreme. She feared that the Prince Imperial's future might be prejudiced.'

On one occasion the Emperor fainted at Marguerite Bellanger's villa, as a result of his exertions and his ill-health. The agitated Empress took her lawyer, Amedée Macquard, with her and drove to the villa of this 'devilish woman'.

'Mademoiselle,' said the indignant Eugénie, 'you are killing the Emperor! We must put an end to this. I'll pay you. Get out! Leave this house tomorrow morning. I repeat, I'll pay you.'

But the Emperor considered himself insulted by Eugénie's intervention. He lectured the Empress and kept Marguerite.

Napoleon III returned to Vichy for the 'cure' every July for several years, at first in the comfortable villa of Strauss 'of Paris', the composer and director of the Paris Opera (no relation of the Strauss family of Vienna, of waltz fame). Later, in his own villa at Vichy, the 'cure' was enlivened by balls and gay receptions. But in 1870 there were no balls and no receptions, the Emperor had attacks of pain and fever, and rested in bed. He returned to St Cloud, and there on 1st July 1870, an important consultation took place.

The discussion, as Dr Barré (one of the less important physicians present) has recorded, was long, serious and impassioned. Dr Lucien Corvisart (nephew of the great Napoleon's favourite physician, and an authority on the digestive tract) and Dr Conneau, the Emperor's personal medical attendants, insisted that the condition present was a mere catarrh of the bladder. Auguste Nélaton, of the Hôpital St Louis, one of the leading surgeons and teachers of surgery of his time, seemed to agree. Modest and friendly, Nélaton was the inventor of a flexible rubber catheter and a pioneer of abdominal surgery in France. On the contrary, Dr Ricord and Professor Germain Sée insisted that only a calculus could produce such signs and symptoms.

Philippe Ricord, born of French parents at Baltimore, came to Paris to study medicine in 1820, and became the leading authority on venereal diseases. He was the first to differentiate (in 1838) gonorrhoea from syphilis, and to divide syphilis into primary, secondary and tertiary stages. Oliver Wendell Holmes called him 'a skeptic as to the morality of the world in general, who would have submitted Diana to treatment with his mineral specifics, and ordered a course of blue pills for the Vestal Virgins'.

Germain Sée, who lived from 1818 to 1896, was then a brilliant young professor in the faculty of medicine of Paris, an authority on nervous diseases, on anaemia, and on diseases of the heart.

'This patient,' said Ricord, 'should have had a sound passed long ago.' 'But,' argued Nélaton, 'why have recourse to this painful procedure? The Emperor is going on very well at present; why torment and upset him? Let us leave him to pass the summer in peace, and it will be time enough to pass a sound when autumn comes.' 'Nevertheless,' insisted Professor Sée, 'if the Emperor were an ordinary patient in your ward in the hospital, what would you do tomorrow morning on your ward round?'

'I should pass a sound,' answered Nélaton.

'Why then,' said Sée, 'incur such a responsibility and not do it at once?'

'My dear colleague,' said Nélaton, 'you are still very young; you do not understand what it is to have the care of a sovereign; he is not a patient like other patients; one has to know when to wait and sometimes dissemble.'

In reality Nélaton knew that his important patient did indeed have a stone in his bladder, but if he recommended waiting it was because he was persuaded that at this time operation was not indicated

In actual fact, the progress of the disease showed that his attitude at the time was correct.

No sound or catheter was passed, and the Empress was not informed about the state of the Emperor's health, though it was agreed by the doctors that a report should be made. When eventually this report was found (on 4th September 1870) among the papers of Dr Conneau at the Tuileries, it had been signed only by Germain Sée, no doubt because of the confusion at the time.

The report stated that the Emperor had a severe anaemia due to a bloody discharge from haemorrhoids, which had been almost constant for six years. In five years he had had four attacks of haematuria. After the illness of 1867 the urine was muco-purulent, but that cleared up. Since August 1869 the urine had continuously contained a certain amount of pus. Dysuria was frequent, and pain was made worse by riding in a carriage or on a horse. A diagnosis of 'calculous pyelocystitis' was made. The doctors agreed that catheterization of the bladder was imperative for the purpose of exploration, and it was considered that the time was opportune as no acute inflammation was present. It seems incredible that only a few days later war was declared, and the sick Emperor set out from St Cloud on active service at the head of his armies, accompanied by the 14-year old Prince Imperial. The French armies were beaten before they began to fight.

At Sedan the Emperor was accompanied by a young doctor, Dr Theophile Auger, assistant to Professor Nélaton, who has left a vivid description: 'The moment that he left the sub-prefecture, a gun-carriage conveyed the wounded Marshal MacMahon. The Emperor asked me to go and look at him. I helped to move the Marshal on to a bed and I saw his wound which I did not consider very serious. I then hurried after the Emperor, who was on horseback and was going towards the battle-field. I rejoined him several hundred yards from the fortifications of Sedan and did not leave him all morning. Twice he came off his horse to pass urine. I saw two of the officers accompanying him shot down near him. The

Emperor re-entered Sedan towards half-past eleven. I did not see him again that day, but on the next day I rejoined him towards half-past seven in the morning at the chateau of Bellevue. Towards ten o'clock, Bismarck and Moltke arrived in a carriage. Half an hour later the capitulation was signed. In the afternoon the Emperor called me and said that since he was going to Cassel as a prisoner of war it was unlikely that he would require my services. He would take with him Conneau and Corvisart and they would be enough.'

Dr James has testified that on the day before and on the day of the battle, Napoleon passed urine that was practically pure blood. And during the battle, Paul de Cassagnac has stated that he saw the Emperor holding on to a tree, trying to struggle with the pain that was torturing him. Later on, in England, Sir William Gull, his physician, was to exclaim, 'How could this man have sat on a horse at Sedan for five hours like that?'

Long afterwards, the Empress Eugénie, in her conversations with M. Paléologue, said: 'Yes, I did know that the Emperor was ill. But of the exact nature of the illness I was entirely ignorant. The doctors themselves did not know it, or at least could not succeed in agreeing on the diagnosis. As for the consultation with Professor Germain Sée, he entrusted his report in a sealed envelope to the Emperor's physician-in-chief, our old friend, Dr Conneau, who did not think fit to show me it. Was he right, or was he wrong? That's another matter. The fact remains that the envelope was not opened until after my husband's death in 1873.

'In that report all the symptoms I had been familiar with, vesical spasms, intense pain in the loins, frequent haematuria, etc., are carefully enumerated, and their origin is attributed to a stone in the bladder. But the other consultant physicians, Nélaton, Ricord, Fauvel, Corvisart and Conneau, did not completely bear out his opinion; they were agreed only on one point, that it was essential to refrain from any local intervention. Conneau, who worshipped my husband, and was deeply devoted to myself, only mentioned rheumatism and cystitis to me. Nay more, he gave me no hint of any particular anxiety when the Emperor assumed the function of generalissimo.'

VII

The war was over in six weeks, and Napoleon III surrendered at Sedan with 39 generals, 2,700 officers and an army of 84,000 men. Bazaine held out for a little longer at Metz and then surrendered with an even larger army of 140,000. Napoleon III was detained at the castle of Wilhelmshohe, near Cassel, along with Dr Conneau and Dr Corvisart, where his health improved. After six months he was allowed to go to England, where the Empress Eugénie had settled down with her household at Camden Place, Chislehurst. It had been found for her by Dr Evans, the American dentist in Paris who had aided the Empress to escape across the Channel, and belonged to a Mr Nathaniel Strode, a wealthy financier and property owner, who by coincidence had long before acted as a trustee for Miss Howard, and he let the furnished house at a modest rental. For eighteen months Napoleon III continued to be in comparatively good health, with the devoted Dr Conneau and his family in residence beside him. But the Bonapartists, stimulated by his ambitious cousin, Prince Napoleon (son of ex-King Jerome), were still active, seeing possibilities of a new 'return from Elba' in the unstable state of France. In the autumn of 1872, however, the health of Napoleon III was such that he could hardly walk, far less ride, as it was assumed that he would have to do, and his consultant physician, Sir William Gull, who had seen him frequently, called in Sir James Paget, surgeon to St Bartholomew's Hospital, who advised consultation with Sir Henry Thompson, the leading specialist in diseases of the bladder.

Sir William Gull was a strong personality, who resembled the great Napoleon in appearance, a resemblance which he was believed to cultivate. Physician to Guy's Hospital, he had an enormous practice and left a very large fortune. He received a baronetcy after his successful attendance on the Prince of Wales (later King Edward VII), who had a serious attack of typhoid fever in 1871. But he was never elected president of the Royal College of Physicians, for his independence and blunt comments made him unpopular with many of his colleagues.

Sir James Paget was one of the chief links between the old pre-Listerian and the new modern surgery. Scrupulously honest and fair-minded, invariably punctual, he was one of the leading surgeons of the day.

Sir Henry Thompson was a vain but talented surgeon, a skilled painter, who exhibited regularly at the Royal Academy, the author of two novels, a pioneer of motoring, the leading advocate of cremation, and celebrated in the social life of London for his 'octaves', dinner parties for eight persons, with eight courses and eight wines, at eight o'clock. King George V, when Prince of Wales, was present at the 300th 'octave'. Surgeon to University College Hospital, he learned lithotrity from Jean Civiale of Paris and soon became its most skilled exponent. He received a knighthood after operating successfully on King Leopold of the Belgians in 1862, and was made a baronet at the age of 70, in 1899.

On Tuesday, 24th December 1872, Sir Henry Thompson accompanied Sir William Gull, along with Dr Conneau, to examine Napoleon III. After passing a flexible catheter, he found that little or no urine was left after micturition and therefore advised that a complete examination should be made without delay under chloroform, as the local sensitivity was extreme. *The Lancet* (of 11th January 1873) reported the case in detail as follows:

'Accordingly, on the 2nd of January, the same party met again at Chislehurst, Mr Clover also being present to give chloroform. His Majesty took it quickly and well. Sir Henry Thompson introduced a sound, and at once detected a large stone. He then introduced a lithotrite, and seized and measured the stone, which he believed to be phosphatic, and as large as a walnut or large chestnut.

The result of the consultation was that, assuming the stone to be phosphatic, it was just within the reach of lithotrity, all the associated conditions – such as sensitive organs, long-standing troubles about the rectum, etc. – considered. But if it should be found to consist of a phosphatic exterior, with uric acid or oxalate of lime beneath, the question of lithotomy would certainly present itself.

'The condition of the urine must be described. It was alkaline, thick and cloudy, depositing a dense layer of pus and mucus, mixed with more or less blood; crystals of triple phosphate and blood and pus-corpuscles were abundant; but there was no other important deviation from the natural standard.

'On January 2nd 1873, at 3.30 p.m. – present Sir William Gull, Sir Henry Thompson, Dr Conneau, Dr le Baron Corvisart, Mr Clover (the leading anaesthetist in London), and Mr Foster (Sir Henry Thompson's assistant). Sir Henry Thompson crushed the stone freely, removing debris largely, which he deemed it important to do under the circumstances of the case. At 6 p.m. there was a slight rigor, followed by the usual febrile phenomena. The urine was clear; but little blood. Slept at intervals during the night. Micturition very frequent.

'The pain and frequency of micturition increased greatly during the next two or three days. The urine became more charged with blood. The pains and irritation of both the bladder and the rectum, of which the tenesmus was constant and distressing, were mitigated but not removed by remedial agents. It was therefore decided to operate again without delay, and to remove the irritating fragments.

'January 6th, 10 a.m. – All were present as before, and everything was arranged for operation at this hour. Just before the time appointed His Majesty was attacked by a rigor, and postponement was necessary. He recovered from the more obvious effects in an hour and a half, and, as it was absolutely essential to relieve the bladder, he was placed under the influence of chloroform by Mr Clover at twelve o'clock. On commencing, a large fragment was found embedded in the prostatic or membranous urethra, entirely preventing the passage of any instrument into the bladder. With a good deal of careful manipulation it was moved so as to permit the introduction of the lithotrite. Its presence had doubtless prevented the spontaneous passing of debris since the first operation. Lithotrity was then performed, and a still larger quantity removed than at the first sitting. It may be added here that His Majesty was rather liable to a rigor on derangements of the internal viscera.

'January 7th. – Small debris passed freely during the night, but micturition very frequent, two or three times within the hour, but sometimes oftener; urine offensive, containing much blood. In the morning it was evident that obstruction existed far back in the urethra. This was verified by the introduction of an instrument, but in the extremely irritable condition of the parts, and as the bladder was sufficiently relieved, it was deemed prudent not to employ any prolonged efforts to dislodge fragments at present.'

The Emperor was watched anxiously through the night of Wednesday, 8th January. He was seen by all his medical attendants at 11 p.m., then at 2 a.m. on Thursday morning by Dr Conneau, at 4 a.m. by Dr Corvisart, and at 6 a.m. by Sir Henry Thompson. He slept soundly through the night. At 9.45 a.m. on Thursday morning he was seen by all the doctors, with the addition of Dr Clover, the 'chloroformist'. There were indications for the need of a further operation and the Emperor appeared so well that it was determined to perform it at noon. His pulse was 84. A change, however, soon occurred. At 10.25 a.m., when Sir Henry Thompson again visited his patient, in company with Dr Conneau and Dr Corvisart, they found him much altered in appearance, his pulse feeble, his breathing slow. The Empress sent for a priest, but the Emperor was too ill to make his confession. Recognizing Dr Conneau, he held out his hand to him and murmured some words about Sedan. He sank rapidly and died without pain at 10.45 a.m. on Thursday, 9th January 1873.

A post-mortem examination of the body was conducted by the

leading expert in London, Dr Burdon Sanderson, professor of pathological anatomy at University College, in the presence of the physicians and surgeons lately in attendance upon the Emperor, and its results were given with fullness and precision in *The Times* (of 11th January 1873) as follows:

'The most important result of the examination was that the kidneys were found to be involved in the inflammatory effects produced by the irritation of the vesical calculus (which must have been in the bladder several years) to a degree which was not suspected; and if it had been suspected could not have been ascertained. The disease of the kidneys was of two kinds: There was, on the one hand, dilation of both ureters, and of the pelves of both kidneys. On the left side the dilatation was excessive, and had given rise to atrophy of the glandular substance of the organ. On the other, there was sub-acute inflammation of the uriniferous tubes which was of more recent origin. The parts in the neighbourhood of the bladder were in a healthy state. The mucous membrane of the bladder and prostatic urethra exhibited signs of sub-acute inflammation, but not the slightest indication of injury. In the interior of the bladder was found a part of a calculus, the form of which indicated that half had been removed. Besides this, there were two or three extremely small fragments none of them larger than a hempseed. This half calculus weighed about three-quarters of an ounce, and measured $1\frac{1}{4}$ inch by $1\frac{5}{16}$ inch. There was no disease of the heart, nor of any other organ excepting the kidneys. The brain and its membranes were in a perfectly natural state. The blood was generally liquid, containing only a very few small clots. No trace of obstruction by coagula could be found either in the venous system, in the heart, or in the pulmonary artery. Death took place by failure of the circulation, and was attributable to the general constitutional state of the patient.

'The disease of the kidneys, of which this state was the expression, was of such a nature and so advanced that it would in any case have shortly determined a fatal result.

'Signed by all present,

J. BURDON SANDERSON, M.D.

DR CONNEAU

DR LE BARON CORVISART

HENRY THOMPSON

J. T. CLOVER

JOHN FOSTER

'Camden-place, Chislehurst, January 10th 1873, 6.30 p.m.'

Sir William Gull left Camden Place as soon as the autopsy was over, and was not present at the careful consideration and discussion of the facts entered upon by the other medical men assembled. He recorded a separate opinion, which he sent to be printed in *The Times*, on the origin of the calculus:

'I desire to express the opinion that the phosphate of lime calculus which formed the nucleus of the mass was the result of prior cystitis (catarrhus vesicae), and not the cause of it. This nucleus was of uncertain duration, and may even have been more recent than supposed in the appended reports.

'However, this may be, it was encrusted by two distinct and more recent formations of crystalline phosphate. The inner incrustation around the amorphous phosphate of lime was dense, and separated from the other incrustation by a looser cellular but crystalline deposit of triple phosphate. It seems to my judgement more in accordance with clinical experience to regard the cystitis as the prior lesion, and that this, by extension, as is common in such cases, affected subsequently the ureters and pelves of the kidneys. No doubt in the later stages of the malady the calculus became, by its formation and increase, an augmenting cause of the lesions.

'The other facts and statements I entirely endorse.

WILLIAM W. GULL, M.D.

'Brook Street, January 10.'

Sir William Gull was severely criticized by his colleagues and in

H

the columns of *The Lancet* for this characteristically independent
addendum, which added little or nothing to the value of the post-
mortem report. But the public, both in England and France, were
weighing and sifting every symptom and incident of the closing
days of the Emperor. *Le Figaro* criticized the short intervals between
Sir Henry Thompson's interventions, and popular opinion in
France blamed the noxious English drug chloroform as having
hastened death. In England *The Lancet* criticized (mistakenly) the
preference for lithotrity over lithotomy, and the public were
shocked to read in *The Times*: 'It is melancholy to think that, not-
withstanding all our discoveries and all our progress, several
celebrated physicians and surgeons are still compelled to put their
hands to a confession that the disease of the kidneys which must so
soon have killed the Emperor existed "to a degree which was not
suspected; and, if it had been suspected, could not have been
ascertained". A man may still, it appears,' said *The Times*, 'die under
the hands of the first doctors of the world of a great organic disease
without their knowledge of anything about it; and the only reflection which is not painful in this agonizing dissection of human
infirmities is that he who endured them now endures them no
longer.'

VIII

The Emperor Napoleon III died of uraemia, and death in any case
could not have been long postponed. There is no doubt that the
stone, which was causing distressing symptoms, had to be removed,
and lithotrity was the safest procedure.

There was a history of pus in the bladder for over three years, and
there was also haematuria, doubtless due to the stone. Only one
kidney was functioning towards the end, and there was pyelone-
phritis (severe infection of the kidneys) on both sides, which would
account for the attacks of rigors. The post-mortem examination
showed that the Emperor did not die of an embolus. The fact that
this was in January 1873, and antiseptic (far less aseptic) surgery

was not yet practised in England, did not really add to the hazards of the operation, as the bladder was already grossly infected.

The lithotrity may indeed have been the last straw to put the kidneys into failure, but obviously something had to be done to relieve the painful and persistent symptoms. The normal urinary tract is remarkably resistant to infection, but if a calculus is present a severe infection may develop which will not clear up until the underlying disease has been successfully treated.

REFERENCES

PRINCE NAPOLEON-LOUIS BONAPARTE. *Des Idées Napoléoniennes,* Colburn, London 1839.

The Lancet: 1873, pages 58–60, 63, 100, 105, 111–14, 141, 188.

The Times: 1873, January to February.

BLANCHARD JERROLD. *Life of Napoleon III,* 4 vols. Longmans, London 1874–82.

A. CORLIEU. *La mort des Rois de France,* Honoré Champion, Paris 1892.

F. A. SIMPSON. *The Rise of Louis Napoleon,* Longmans, London 1909. *idem: Louis Napoleon and the Recovery of France,* Longmans, London 1923.

PHILIP GUEDALLA. *The Second Empire,* Hodder & Stoughton, London 1922.

OCTAVE AUBRY. *Napoleon III,* Fayard, Paris 1929. *idem: Eugénie, Empress of the French,* Trans. by F. M. Atkinson, Cobden-Sanderson, London 1939.

M. PALÉOLOGUE. *The Tragic Empress – Intimate Conversations with the Empress Eugénie,* Trans. by H. Miles, Butterworth, London 1929.

ROBERT SENCOURT. *Napoleon III: the Modern Emperor,* Benn, London 1933.

GEORGES LECOMTE. *Napoleon III, sa maladie, son déclin,* Ciba, Lyon 1937.

J. M. THOMPSON. *Louis Napoleon and the Second Empire*, Blackwell, Oxford 1956.

SIMONE ANDRÉ MAUROIS. *Miss Howard and the Emperor*, Trans. by H. Hare, Collins, London 1957.

DAVID H. PINKNEY. *Napoleon III and the Rebuilding of Paris*, Princeton University Press, 1958

ALFRED COBBAN. *A History of Modern France*, Vol. 2, 1799–1945. Pelican Books, London 1961.

T. A. B. CORLEY. *Democratic Despot: a life of Napoleon III*, Barrie & Rockliff, London 1961.

CHAPTER VIII

THE LAMENESS OF LORD BYRON

BYRON, the aristocratic rebel, has had much more influence on the Continent than in his native country. Although his fellow-countrymen admired his poetry they jeered at his politics, but abroad his outspoken hatred of tyranny and defence of the oppressed made him a hero and inspired a whole series of revolutionary movements – in France, Germany, Italy, Russia, Hungary, Poland and Greece. Alfred de Musset considered that after Napoleon, Byron and Goethe were the greatest geniuses of the century.

On the break-up of Byron's marriage in 1816, his voluntary exile from England and his conception of Man engaged in a tragic and romantic war against the Universe, made him the leading figure of the European romantic movement. One of the chief influences upon this attitude was his bitter resentment of the fact that, in spite of his acknowledged genius and his wonderfully good looks, he was a cripple. But what caused his lameness and exactly what type of deformity it was, are still puzzles.

II

Born in London at 16 Holles Street, Cavendish Square, on 22nd January 1788, George Gordon Byron's earliest recollections were of quarrels between his parents. His father ran through both his previous wife's and Byron's mother's fortunes and died penniless at Valenciennes. His mother (who was a Gordon of Gight, descended from King James I of Scotland) retired to Aberdeen in shabby gentility, and sent her son for four years to Aberdeen Grammar

School. He told Lady Holland long afterwards that his childhood had been made miserable by his mother calling him 'a lame brat'. He feared his mother for her violent and capricious temper and her cruelty; a wicked though Calvinistic nurse stimulated his sexual precocity; and his lameness filled him with shame and prevented him from being 'one of the herd' at school. Tom Moore later noted Byron's 'anguish' on overhearing the 'once worshipped' Mary Chaworth say to her maid: 'Do you think I could care anything for that lame boy?'

At the age of 10, after having lived in comparative poverty, he inherited from his great-uncle the family title and two large estates at Rochdale and in Nottinghamshire, along with the half-ruined Newstead Abbey. His great-uncle, 'the wicked Lord Byron', had killed his cousin Mr Chaworth in a duel or rather a scuffle with swords in a dark room lit by a single candle. He was convicted of manslaughter before the House of Lords in 1765, but was exempted from punishment because he was a peer. He was also said (though on less certain evidence) to have shot his coachman in a frenzy of rage.

Byron's mother said that the great John Hunter saw the boy in London when he was born and prescribed for the infant's feet; he made the characteristically sensible remark that 'It will do very well in time.' In Nottingham she turned her son over to a quack named Lavender, who was truss-maker to the local hospital. He placed the affected foot in a vice-like contraption and tried to twist it forcibly into normal shape. The only result of this painful treatment was an acute – though fortunately, only temporary – aggravation of the boy's congenital lameness.

He was sent to a preparatory school in Dulwich and then, by the advice of his guardian, Lord Carlisle, on to Harrow, where he played cricket for the school against Eton on 12th August 1805; he made 11 runs ('notches' they were called then) in the first innings and seven in the second innings – only two of the team got more, and Eton won the match. Then he went briefly to Cambridge, where he made some life-long friends, especially John Cam Hobhouse, afterwards Lord Broughton.

Hours of Idleness, a book of verses published in 1808, were mere juvenilia, written when he was 19, but gave rise (after a severely critical review in the *Edinburgh Review*, by Brougham, not by Jeffrey, as the poet believed) to the brilliantly satirical *English Bards and Scotch Reviewers*. He was determined, once he came of age and funds were available, to make his Grand Tour in the Near East, and after visiting – by way of Gibraltar and Spain – Italy, Greece, Turkey and Asia Minor in company with his highly respectable friend Hobhouse, *Childe Harold* was the dazzling result: it opened a new world to his English readers.

In the early months of 1812 Byron had taken his seat in the House of Lords and made two or three promising speeches on the side of the workers against new and severe laws relating to the introduction of machinery. Then on 10th March, 1812, *Childe Harold* was published, and at the age of 24 Byron 'woke up to find himself famous'. Of *The Corsair*, published in 1814, John Murray sold 10,000 copies on the day of publication. As his poems were published they were translated at once into French, Italian, German and Russian. *Manfred* had 33 translations in 12 different languages. Byron's violent affair with the unbalanced and self-advertising Lady Caroline Lamb lasted for barely three months, and in January 1815, he married Miss Annabella Milbanke, the daughter of a baronet and reputed to be an heiress. He was accused afterwards of having married her for her money, but the £10,000 (some say £20,000) which she had soon melted away in the extravagant life they led, and Byron was before long in financial difficulties. The Newstead estate, though said to be worth £150,000, brought in an income of only £1,500 a year, and was put up for sale, while the Rochdale estate was involved in a lawsuit.

A daughter was born in December 1815, but in January 1816, Lady Byron went home to her father and demanded a separation from her husband, alleging all manner of eccentricities and infidelities, which were very probably true. The accusation of incest with his half-sister, Mrs Leigh, though whispered about in society, was made not then but for the first time publicly in 1869, when Harriet Beecher Stowe (author of *Uncle Tom's Cabin*) published a book called *Lady Byron Vindicated*, which gave Lady Byron's side of the story 'as related by her to Mrs Stowe'. Many other books have since been published on one side or the other, and there is still a mass of private papers in the possession of the Lovelace family (descendants of Byron's daughter: the Earl of Lytton is Byron's great-great-grandson), in which the truth may yet be found. In any case, on 25th April 1816, Byron left England for ever and thereafter lived mainly in Venice, Ravenna, Genoa and Pisa.

The last canto of *Childe Harold* was published in April 1818, and in September of that year he began the composition of his master-piece, the mock-heroic *Don Juan*, the publication of which con-tinued until 1823. But in March 1823, he heard that he had been elected to the 'Greek Committee', a group of liberals who had taken up the cause of Greek emancipation, and resolved to go to Greece, where he offered his personal services and large sums of money to help the insurgents. He spent three months at Misso-longhi, trying to reconcile various factions among the rebels, his health broke down, he was soaked to the skin by rain when out riding, and he contracted a fever (probably malaria) and rheumatism. He died on 19th April 1824, aged 36. His body was embalmed and brought back to England, where it is buried in the family vault in the parish church of Hucknall, near Newstead Abbey.

III

The degree of Byron's disability is difficult to estimate. He was able to play cricket, he boxed (a pupil of the famous Gentleman Jackson), and he swam well enough to swim the Hellespont on a memorable occasion. But he certainly walked with a peculiar limp or 'sliding gait'. The consensus of medical opinion (so writes mistakenly Dr

P. M. Dale of Los Angeles) is that Byron suffered from clubfoot of
the equinovarus type involving the right foot. Thomas Moore,
Byron's first biographer, and John Cam Hobhouse, his close friend,
both asserted that it was the right foot that was deformed. His
boxing instructor, Gentleman Jackson, thought that it was his left
foot. John Galt, also his biographer and companion on one of his
Eastern tours, Lady Blessington and the Countess Guiccioli, both
of them intimate friends, could never make up their minds which
foot was deformed. Mrs Leigh Hunt, who with her impecunious
husband was for long a guest of Byron, thought that 'the left foot
was shrunken but that it was not club foot'. Leigh Hunt, incidentally, ungratefully described Byron as 'hopping about like a bird'.

In her *Recollections* of Lord Byron, the Countess Guiccioli wrote
of Byron's lameness: 'By an accident which occurred at the time
of his birth, one of his feet was twisted out of its natural position,
and, to restore the limb to shape, expedients were used under the
direction of the celebrated Dr Hunter. Mary Gray (his nurse), to
whom fell the task of putting on the bandages at bed-time, used to
sing him to sleep.'

E. J. Trelawny, in his *Recollections of the last days of Shelley and
Byron*, published in 1858, wrote vividly as follows (page 223):
'No one was in the house but Fletcher [Byron's valet], of which I
was glad. As if he knew my wishes, he led me up a narrow stair into
a small room, with nothing in it but a coffin standing on trestles.
No word was spoken by either of us; he withdrew the black pall and
the white shroud, and there lay the embalmed body of the Pilgrim –
more beautiful in death than in life. The contraction of the muscles
and skin had effaced every line that time or passion had ever traced
on it; few marble busts could have matched its stainless white, the
harmony of its proportions, and perfect finish; yet he had been
dissatisfied with that body, and longed to cast its slough. How often
I had heard him curse it! He was jealous of the genius of Shakespeare
– that might well be – but where had he seen the face or form worthy
to excite his envy? I asked Fletcher to bring me a glass of water

On his leaving the room, to confirm or remove my doubts as to the cause of his lameness, I uncovered the Pilgrim's feet, and was answered – the great mystery was solved. Both his feet were clubbed, and his legs withered to the knee – the form and features of an Apollo, with the feet and legs of a sylvan satyr. This was a curse, chaining a proud and soaring spirit like his to the dull earth . . . His deformity was always uppermost in his thoughts, and influenced every act of his life, spurred him on to poetry, as that was one of the few paths to fame open to him – and as if to be revenged on Nature for sending him into the world "scarce half made up", he scoffed at her works and traditions with the pride of Lucifer; this morbid feeling ultimately goaded him on to his last Quixotic crusade in Greece.

'Knowing and sympathising with Byron's sensitiveness, his associates avoided prying into the cause of his lameness; so did strangers, from good breeding or common humanity. It was generally thought his halting gait originated in some defect of the right foot or ankle – the right foot was the most distorted, and it had been made worse in his boyhood by vain efforts to set it right. He told me that for several years he wore steel splints, which so wrenched the sinews and tendons of his leg that they increased his lameness; the foot was twisted inwards, only the edge touched the ground, and that leg was shorter than the other. His shoes were peculiar – very high heeled, with the soles uncommonly thick on the inside and pared thin on the outside – the toes were stuffed with cotton-wool, and his trousers were very large below the knee and strapped down so as to cover his feet. The peculiarity of his gait was now accounted for; he entered a room with a sort of run, as if he could not stop, then planted his best leg well forward, throwing back his body to keep his balance.'

The description of 'the form and features of an Apollo, with the feet and legs of a satyr' has been much quoted, and the *Dictionary of National Biography* took Trelawny, who had known Byron only for a few months, as its authority on Byron's lameness. Mrs Langley

Moore, however, in her recent biography of Lord Byron, points out that in fact Byron's tin-lined coffin, after his embalmment, had been hermetically sealed on 25th April (as is shown in the official document published in Sir Harold Nicolson's *Byron, the Last Journey*) and Trelawny could not have arrived before the 26th. Trelawny himself states that he arrived at Missolonghi on the 24th or 25th April, and that Byron had died on the 19th. Trelawny wrote to Colonel Stanhope two days after his arrival: 'I have been employed in arranging the affairs of my lost friend, sealing papers, and his body is in spirits.' H. J. Massingham writes: 'The only explanation seems to be Trelawny did not know that he was lying; in other words, that he wrote about Byron's feet not as they were but as he expected to find them.'

J. J. Jeaffreson wrote in 1883: 'The lameness was due to the contraction of the tendon Achilles of each foot, which, preventing him from putting his heels to the ground, compelled him to walk on the balls and toes of his feet. Both feet may have been equally well formed, save in this sinew, till one of them was subjected to injudicious surgery; the right being, however, considerably smaller than the left. Instead of being congenital, the slight contraction of the left tendon Achilles may have been the result of the patient's habit of stepping only on the fore part of the foot, so as to accommodate its movements to the action of the other extremity. . . .

'It is therefore manifest,' concludes Jeaffreson, 'that Byron's lameness was of a kind far more afflicting to the body and vexatious to the spirits than the lameness of such an ordinary club-foot as disfigured Sir Walter Scott.'

The Countess Guiccioli denied with vigour that Byron had been crippled in the manner Trelawny described, pointing out that 'it would have been utterly impossible to have concealed such a deformity in infancy or schooldays and that he had always mounted a horse with remarkable elegance, swam better than any swimmer of his time, and played games with dexterity . . . One must further add – did he always make love then platonically?'

When he climbed a cliff with the Countess Guiccioli, wrote Austin K. Gray, his face was drawn and white with pain and he leaned heavily on her arm as they walked. She bathed his foot on their return to the house.

Thomas Medwin, in his *Journal of the Conversations of Lord Byron*, quotes Forrester, who served with Byron at Missolonghi: 'Lord Byron is, as near as I can judge, about five feet nine inches in height and of an athletic make, which is most apparent from the loins downward, the breast having suffered from the attitude acquired through his lameness.' Dr Julius Millingen, who was also at Missolonghi, in his *Memoirs* states on the other hand that the *upper* portion of Byron's body was fine and well developed. Forrester, by the way, is responsible for this delightful story of Byron: 'On opening a bottle of wine, and inspecting the complexion of its contents, his lordship questioned Fletcher his valet, as to its name and lineage. "I really don't know, my lord," was the reply. "Then away with it," he rejoined, "I hate anonymous wine."'

When the Countess Guiccioli first met Byron she found his face pale, it sagged under the jaw, there were dark lines under his eyes and a peevish droop at the corner of his mouth. He was fat, his hands were small and white and plump, and he limped. 'But she saw nothing of all that. She saw only his small, well-shaped head – with the curling hair – that nose, those eyes, those lips – the beauty of feature and expression that lay behind a tired and dissipated face.'

IV

At a 'social meeting' of the Royal Society of Medicine in London on 21st March 1923, Dr H. C. Cameron, then paediatric physician to Guy's Hospital, discussed the subject of Byron's lameness and came to the conclusion that Byron suffered from a mild case of Little's disease. This is a spastic type of paralysis due usually to incomplete development of the pyramidal tracts of the brain or to brain injury incurred during the birth process. Dr Cameron exhibited two surgical boots which he was sure had been made for and worn by Byron (they were lent by Sir John Murray). Both boots were for the right foot, but they were adapted to a long, slender foot and not to a club-foot.

Mr James Kemble, surgeon and writer on medical history, in the *West London Medical Journal* described two boots in the possession of the publishing firm of John Murray, both of which are for the right foot: one was said to have been fitted when the poet was 11 years of age, the other when he was 18. 'The soles of these boots,' wrote Kemble, 'were wedged in a manner indicating that they were intended to compensate a varus type of club foot, that is, one in which the sole of the foot turns inward to face the opposite foot. Another boot was believed to have been worn over the corrective boot, which belief, if well founded, may account for some of the confusion with respect to the type of the deformity.'

More recently, Sir Denis Browne, the orthopaedic surgeon, of Great Ormond Street Children's Hospital, showed at a discussion at the Royal Society of Medicine on 1st December 1959, photographs of two devices worn by Byron when he was approaching manhood; they are in the possession of Sir John Murray, the direct descendant of Byron's original publisher. They had been photographed before, but not in such a way as to bring out their true nature. Sir Denis Browne came to the conclusion that these devices did not aim at correcting a deformity but at disguising it. What had to be disguised was a grotesquely thin calf and a small foot, a failure of the region to form properly; a dysplasia and not a moulding deformity such as a club-foot. The legging which he illustrated had thick padding which would give the effect of a normal calf inside the long trousers from which Byron refused to be parted in public, apparently even when swimming. The inner boot that surrounded the foot would fill up the lasts that are still in existence, and so make the two feet alike in ordinary use.

None of the treatment, painful and embarrassing though it was, that Byron suffered as a boy, could have had the slightest influence on his deformity. Those surgeons who have struggled with congenital deformities of the feet will realize that none of it could have altered in any way their stubborn tendency to resume their original form.

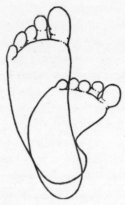

Outline of a true club foot, superimposed on tracing of the foot that would fit Byron's inner shoe (after Denis Browne: *Proceedings of the Royal Society of Medicine,* 1960, **53**, 441).

The foot itself, insisted Sir Denis Browne, was not in the least like a club-foot, so called because if untreated it contracts and turns upside down into a rounded club-like lump; it was on the contrary a long narrow foot in slight metatarsal varus, that is, with a bend inwards towards the middle of its length. Feet of this dysplasic kind are always stiff, so there would be a lack of ankle movement, which would account for Byron's 'sliding gait' described by one of the few accurate observers.

REFERENCES

THOMAS MEDWIN. *Journal of the Conversations of Lord Byron,* 2 vols, Colburn, London 1824.

T. SHELDRAKE. Lancet, 1827–28, Vol. *ii*, p. 779.

JULIUS MILLINGEN. *Memoirs of the Affairs of Greece*, Rodwell, London 1831.

E. J. TRELAWNY. *Recollections of the last days of Shelley and Byron*, Moxon, London 1858.

ANON. *My Recollections of Lord Byron*, 2 vols. Richard Bentley, London 1869.
'The publisher of this translation feels authorized to state, that it is the production of the celebrated Countess Guiccioli.'

HARRIET BEECHER STOWE. *Lady Byron Vindicated*, Sampson Low, London 1869.

J. J. JEAFFRESON. *The Real Lord Byron*, 2 vols. Hurst & Blackett, London 1883.

H. C. CAMERON. *British Medical Journal*, 1923, 21st March, vol. *i*, p. 564.

HAROLD NICOLSON. *Byron, the Last Journey*, Constable, London 1924.

H. J. MASSINGHAM. *The Friend of Shelley: a memoir of Edward John Trelawny*, Cobden-Sanderson, London 1930.

BERTRAND RUSSELL. *History of Western Philosophy*, Chapter XXIII, 'Byron'. Allen & Unwin, London 1946.

AUSTIN K. GRAY. *Teresa, the Story of Byron's Last Mistress*, Harrap, London 1948.

JAMES KEMBLE. *The lameness of Lord Byron*. West London Medical Journal, Vol. 40, page 33. 1935.

P. M. DALE. *Medical Biographies*, University of Oklahoma Press, Norman, U.S.A. 1952.

DENIS BROWNE. Proceedings of the Royal Society of Medicine, 1960, June, Vol. 53, p. 440.

DORIS LANGLEY MOORE. *The Late Lord Byron*, John Murray, London 1961.

CHAPTER IX

NAPOLEON ON ST HELENA

NAPOLEON was sent to the lonely island of St Helena in the South Atlantic because the victorious Allies did not know what to do with him. He was, it must be remembered, only 45, and still at the height of his powers. Elba had proved too near, he had reconquered France without firing a shot in twenty days, and Waterloo, as the Duke of Wellington said, had been 'a damned close-run thing'. Lord Liverpool, the Prime Minister, wrote to Lord Castlereagh, his Foreign Secretary: 'We wish that the King of France would hang or shoot Buonaparte, as the best termination of the business.'

After Waterloo, which was fought on 18th June 1815, Napoleon returned to Paris, where the Council of Ministers refused to support him any longer and appointed a Commission of Five, with Fouché as president, who gave him the alternatives of abdication or dethronement. Napoleon chose to abdicate (for the second time) and a few days later set out for the seaport of Rochefort, where he went on board a French frigate intending to sail to America. But the British Navy was alerted and had instructions to capture him and take him to England. He therefore surrendered with his entourage of 33 persons to Captain Maitland of H.M.S. *Bellerophon*, which sailed to Torbay.

Captain Maitland afterwards published in his *Narrative* the well-known letter addressed by Napoleon to the Prince Regent, of which the following is a translation:

'Your Royal Highness,

A victim of the factions which distract my country, and to the emnity of the greatest powers of Europe, I have terminated my

political career, and I come, like Themistocles, to throw myself upon
the hospitality of the British people. I put myself under the protection of their laws; which I claim from your Royal Highness, as the
most powerful, the most constant, and the most generous of my
enemies.

Rochefort, 13th July, 1815.

(signed) NAPOLEON.'

Maitland wrote of Napoleon: 'I therefore, once for all, beg to
state most distinctly that, from the time of his coming on board my
ship, to the period of his quitting her, his conduct was invariably
that of a gentleman; and in no one instance do I recollect him to
have made use of a rude expression, or to have been guilty of any
kind of ill-breeding.'

Napoleon apparently hoped and expected that he would be
allowed to live in England 'as a country gentleman', but the British
Government was negotiating with its allies and had very different
intentions. Treaties were signed with Austria, Prussia and Russia
that responsibility for the safe-keeping of Napoleon was to devolve
upon Great Britain. Lord Liverpool wrote to the Foreign Secretary:
'We are all decidedly of the opinion that it would not answer to
confine him in this country. Very nice legal questions might arise
upon the subject, which would be particularly embarrassing. But,
independent of these considerations, you know enough of the feelings of people in this country not to doubt he would become an
object of curiosity immediately, and possibly of compassion, in the
course of a few months; and the circumstances of being here, or
indeed, anywhere in Europe, would contribute to keep up a certain
degree of ferment in France.'

Lord Liverpool favoured the choice of St Helena, which had,
indeed, been mentioned long before at the Congress of Vienna,
after Napoleon had been sent to Elba. 'The situation is particularly
healthy,' he wrote, 'there is only one place in the circuit of the island
where ships can anchor . . . At such a distance and in such a place,

I

all intrigue would be impossible, and being withdrawn so far from the European world, he would very soon be forgotten.'

Napoleon protested about being sent to 'an island within the tropics: they might as well have signed my death-warrant at once'. But there are worse places than St Helena, though it is 1,200 miles from the nearest mainland, Capetown is 1,750 miles distant and England 4,400 miles. It is ten miles long and over six miles broad, 47 square miles in area, several times larger than Gibraltar, and about the same size as Jersey, in the Channel Islands. The climate is subtropical, there are high mountains and pleasant valleys, part of the island is well wooded, vegetation profuse, and the soil fertile, though some of it is rocky and barren. The country houses have beautiful lawns and gardens. There is but one small town, Jamestown, a port on a river, with shops, stores, boarding-houses and a hotel, a short street, the Marino, along the wharf, and the main street, about a mile long, at right angles to it. In 1815 the inhabitants of the island, in addition to the garrison of over a thousand, numbered between two and three thousand, many of them negro slaves, and some Chinese. At that time it belonged to the East India Company, for whom it was a port of call on the way to Cape Colony, and the power of appointing the Governor was vested in its Court of Directors; but when it was chosen for the detention of Napoleon the Governor, though appointed by the Court of Directors, was nominated by the Government.

The partisans of Napoleon have emphasized the unhealthiness of the climate of St Helena and it was even suggested that it was chosen with the deliberate intention of shortening his life. 'Hepatitis' was said to be endemic, but it is doubtful whether this meant anything more then than the 'liver' ailment common to European inhabitants of India and the East, due mainly to lack of exercise and excess of alcohol. General Gourgaud, who accompanied Napoleon, wrote from St Helena to his mother (in a recently discovered letter) on 12th January 1816: 'The climate here is very mild, the air very healthy; the change of seasons is only very slightly felt. It is

perpetual spring; in short, dear mother, I am very well physically
... We are now quite settled in a pretty country house.'

II

Napoleon was to sail to St Helena in H.M.S. *Northumberland*, more
seaworthy than the old *Bellerophon*, flying the flag of Rear-Admiral
Sir George Cockburn, and he was to choose from his suite three
officers to accompany him, along with his personal surgeon and
twelve servants. Admiral Lord Keith decided that he might also
take Las Cases, who spoke English fluently, as his secretary, and
that the others might take their families and servants. Altogether,
then, Napoleon was accompanied by 26 persons when he transferred from the *Bellerophon* to the *Northumberland*.

Count Henri Bertrand had been with Napoleon on Elba, previously with his army as a general of engineers, and had become
Grand Marshal of the palace. He had a considerable fortune, which
he had wisely transferred to England before he was proscribed by
the Bourbons. His wife, who disliked intensely the life at St Helena,
was partly of Irish and partly Creole ancestry (said to be related to
the Empress Josephine) and they had three children – a fourth was
born at St Helena. General Charles Montholon was a Marquis whose
stepfather had been ambassador to Turkey, and he had known the
Bonaparte family in Corsica (though probably more slightly than he
suggested). He boasted of his military exploits, but in fact his
career had been undistinguished until he attached himself to
Napoleon after Waterloo. His wife was three years older than her
husband, had been divorced by a Swiss financier, and is said to have
become Napoleon's mistress at St Helena. They had one son.
General Gaspard Gourgaud was a brave soldier who had been
orderly officer to Napoleon in his later campaigns and was created
a Baron of the Empire. He was unmarried, and was of a jealous,
moody, self-torturing nature, offended when Napoleon showed
favour to any of his companions.

The Marquis de Las Cases belonged to the old nobility, whose estates had been confiscated during the Revolution. He had been a naval officer and went to England, where he spent ten years, supporting himself by teaching French and writing a successful 'historical atlas'. He attached himself to Napoleon (who hardly knew him) after his return from Elba and accompanied the Emperor to St Helena as his secretary, with the deliberate intention of writing a book about him – which, in fact, when it was published, had an enormous success. He was accompanied to St Helena by his son, an intelligent boy of 15.

Napoleon had intended to take with him as his personal physician Dr Louis Maingault, recommended by his famous physician Baron Corvisart; but Maingault declined when he heard that they were going to St Helena, not the United States. On board the *Bellerophon*, however, Napoleon had made the acquaintance of the senior naval surgeon, Dr Barry O'Meara, who spoke Italian fluently, and, being favourably impressed, invited him, the day before the *Northumberland* sailed, to accompany him to St Helena. O'Meara was an Irish Protestant, born in 1786 and educated at Trinity College, Dublin, and destined to attend Napoleon for three years. He had first joined the Army and served in Italy as a surgeon to the 62nd Regiment, but had to resign after having acted as second in a duel, and then served as a naval surgeon in *Goliath* and *Bellerophon*.

Admiral Lord Keith sent for O'Meara and advised him to accept the appointment 'though he could not order him to do so, as it was foreign to the naval service, and a business altogether extraordinary'. O'Meara stipulated that he should be 'always considered a British officer and upon the list of naval surgeons on full pay, paid by the British Government, and that he should be at liberty to quit so peculiar a service, should he find it not to be consonant to his wishes'. It has been said that O'Meara acted in St Helena as a 'double agent', taking the side of Napoleon yet supplying the British Government with information obtained from him; but it is more probable that his letters to his friend Finlaison, an Admiralty official, which he was aware were being read by the First Lord of the

Admiralty, were hoped merely to help his advancement in the service, and he was certainly not paid for spying.

Of the servants, the most important was Louis Marchand, *premier valet de chambre*, who had been with the Emperor at Elba. He used to read to Napoleon when he could not sleep, and he was one of the executors of his will, along with Bertrand and Montholon. Napoleon III, who never forgot a service, made him a Count of the Second Empire. Cipriani Franceshi was *maître d'hotel*; he was a Corsican and had an old family connection with the Bonapartes – his daughter was in the service of Napoleon's mother. Louis St Denis was known as 'Ali' because he had formerly served the Emperor in the costume of a Mameluke, and he had enough education to be in charge of the library. Jean Abram Noverraz, Swiss *valet de chambre* since 1809, had served Napoleon at Elba as well as at St Helena. The other servants were of less importance.

III

The voyage took ten weeks but was in pleasant weather, Napoleon ate at the Admiral's table along with his suite, and spent most of his time in his cabin dictating his memoirs to Las Cases. St Helena was reached on 15th October, 1815. It was intended that Napoleon should live at Longwood, the residence of the Lieutenant-Governor (an appointment which was to be abolished on the arrival of the new Governor), and as alterations and additions were to be made to the house, he stayed for a few weeks in the annexe of a cottage called 'The Briars', which belonged to a Mr Balcombe, a subordinate official of the East India Company. Mr Balcombe and his wife had two young daughters, who spoke French and called their visitor 'Boney'. Napoleon seemed to enjoy romping with them, and Betsy Balcombe, who in 1832 married a Mr Abell, later on published her girlish reminiscences of St Helena. After the death of her husband Napoleon III presented her with an estate in Algeria.

Longwood has been unkindly (and inaccurately) described as a cowshed; but although it was originally built in 1753 as a cowhouse and a barn, it was transformed in 1787 into a dwelling-house suitable for the Lieutenant-Governor. It was a fairly large, low group of buildings, only one of them with two stories, standing in its own grounds. To receive Napoleon with his suite and servants substantial additions were made, so that eventually there were 36 rooms on the ground floor as well as a number of attics. A large antechamber, at first the dining-room, was the billiard-room, in which Napoleon did most of his dictating. From the antechamber a door led to the drawing-room, next was the dining-room, and then the library, containing 3,370 volumes. Napoleon's private quarters consisted of a bedroom and a study, a bathroom and a valet's bedroom. At first poorly furnished, in a few months adequate furniture arrived from England.

Napoleon's household now consisted of 16 principals (men, women and children) and 38 servants, many of whom had not enough work to do. Grand Marshal Bertrand and his family had their own new house, Hut's Gate, near by. General Montholon and his wife had five rooms and a bathroom; Las Cases and his son had three small rooms; Gourgaud, Dr O'Meara and Captain Poppleton, the British orderly officer appointed by the Governor, had two rooms each. There was a servants' hall opposite the kitchen, and most of the servants slept in the attics.

The dining-room was lit by wax candles in silver candelabra, the table service was of silver, and the dessert service was of exquisite Sèvres china, with gold knives, forks and spoons. In Napoleon's bedroom was a silver ewer and washbasin.

St Helena was defended by 2,784 officers and men, over 500 guns and a number of mortars. In full view of Longwood House 500 soldiers were permanently stationed. Six brigs circumnavigated the island day and night, and three frigates and two armed vessels lay off Jamestown, ready for immediate action. A garrison continued to be maintained at St Helena until Mr Haldane abolished it in 1907.

IV

Colonel Mark Wilks, the Governor, was in charge of the administration of St Helena, while Admiral Sir George Cockburn, who
was in command of the flotilla based on St Helena, was responsible
for the custody of Napoleon and his suite. With both of them the
Emperor maintained friendly relations, except for an occasional
flare-up when they addressed him as 'General Bonaparte', as the
British Government insisted that he should be called. The atmo-
sphere changed, however, with the arrival on 14th April 1816, of
Lieut.-General Sir Hudson Lowe, the new Governor, who took
over the duties of both Colonel Wilks and Admiral Cockburn. Two
days after his arrival Lowe called to pay his compliments on 'General
Bonaparte' at Longwood at a little before the unseasonable hour of
9 a.m., in a storm of rain and wind. Napoleon, who was still in bed,
sent out word that he was not a 'General', that his Grand Marshal
was not in attendance and had received no notice of the visit, and
that in any case it was too early for an official call. After waiting for
a few minutes Lowe departed in high dudgeon. A later appointment
was made, but the ill-feeling persisted and continued to persist
throughout the half-dozen visits that Lowe made in the next few
months, ending on 18th August, when Napoleon was in such a
violent temper that Lowe walked out, slamming the door behind
him. During the remaining five years of the captivity they never met
again, though from time to time they carried on an acrimonious
correspondence.

Parliament had passed in April 1816, two Acts regarding the
captivity of Napoleon: (1) 'An Act for the more effectually detaining
in custody Napoleon Bonaparte', and (2) 'An Act for regulating the
intercourse with the Island of St Helena during the time Napoleon
Buonaparte shall be detained there'. A warrant was issued to Sir
Hudson Lowe, 'empowering and requiring him safely to detain
and keep Napoleon Bonaparte as a prisoner of war in the island of
St Helena during his Majesty's pleasure, and to treat and deal with

him as a prisoner of war . . . and in case of the escape or rescue of the said Napoleon Bonaparte, to retake, detain, and keep him in custody'. Much of the ill-feeling between Lowe and Napoleon was due to his meticulous interpretation of this warrant.

Hudson Lowe's father was an army surgeon who became 'Surgeon-Major and head of the medical department' in the garrison of Gibraltar from the outbreak of war with France in 1793 until 1801. Hudson Lowe himself was born in Galway in 1769, and had spent his life in the Army, most of it on foreign service. Colonel Hudson Lowe was fortunate in being sent with the news of Napoleon's abdication (before Elba) to England, and for this was knighted by the Prince Regent and promoted to Major-General. He was appointed Quartermaster-General to the British troops in the Low Countries, where (when Napoleon escaped from Elba) he came directly under the orders of the Duke of Wellington. But soon afterwards he was given the command of the British troops at Genoa, and left Belgium at the beginning of June, so missing the battle of Waterloo, at which his successor, General de Lancy, was killed. He arrived in Genoa on 17th June, and when on 1st August he unexpectedly received the information that he was to be entrusted with the custody of Napoleon at St Helena, he left immediately for London. He was given the local rank of Lieutenant-General and a salary of £12,000 per annum.

His instructions from Earl Bathurst, the Secretary at War (and for the Colonies) concluded: 'Many things, however, must be determined by local circumstances; and the experience which I have already had of your judgement and discretion makes me repose this most important trust, without apprehension, in your hands. You will observe that the desire of his Majesty's Government is to allow every indulgence to General Buonaparte which may be compatible with the entire security of his person: that he should not by any means escape, or hold communication with any person whatever (excepting through your agency), must be your unremitted care; and these points being made sure, every resource and amusement which may serve to reconcile Buonaparte to his confinement may be permitted.'

Another letter from Lord Bathurst stated: 'As a general rule, that, although it was the intention of his Majesty's Government that the apartments occupied by Napoleon Buonaparte should be sufficiently furnished, yet needless expenses were to be avoided carefully, and the furniture should be solid and well chosen, without being profusely ornamental.'

On 17th June 1816, there arrived Rear-Admiral Sir Pulteney Malcolm, to succeed Admiral Cockburn in the naval command at St Helena, accompanied by his wife and by the three Commissioners who had been appointed by the Allied Powers. The Marquis de Montchenu represented the French Government of the restoration; he was an undistinguished member of an aristocratic family, an old enemy of Napoleon, cynically appointed a Commissioner by Talleyrand. The Russian Commissioner, Count Balmain, was a cultured and witty diplomat, who had served as a liaison officer on Wellington's staff; at St Helena he married the stepdaughter of Sir Hudson Lowe. Baron Stürmer, the Austrian Commissioner, was a young man who had been a secretary in the Austrian legation at Constantinople. The Prussian Government, from motives of economy, had refused to appoint a Commissioner.

They had been instructed by their Governments 'to assure themselves of Buonaparte's presence on the island and to ascertain if he was properly guarded'. But unfortunately they had not brought any official documents from their respective sovereigns, and Napoleon consistently refused ever to interview them. All that they were able to do was to see the Emperor at a distance.

V

Everybody on St Helena kept a diary or wrote their reminiscences. In 1823 there was published in French and in English, in seven volumes, the work titled in English 'Memoirs of the History of France during the reign of Napoleon, dictated by the Emperor at St Helena to the Generals who shared his captivity; and published from the original manuscripts corrected by himself'. The preface is signed 'A.B.', and it is believed that Las Cases wrote the earlier part and Montholon the greater part of the notes; Gourgaud would have written more of it if he had remained at St Helena. *Letters from the Cape*, a slim volume which caused a sensation, dictated by Napoleon himself to Las Cases, was published in 1817, after Las Cases had been sent away from St Helena in December, 1816, for attempting to carry on a clandestine correspondence, and had spent nearly eight months at Capetown before sailing for Europe.

The '*Memorial*' by Las Cases was published in French in eight volumes in 1823-24 and in English in five volumes; the author realized from it over £80,000 – at a time when the £ was worth more than four times its value today and income tax was non-existent. Napoleon himself urged his household to record his utterances: 'Yesterday evening,' wrote Gourgaud, 'the Emperor told me that I might turn my leisure to profit in writing down his sayings. I would thus gain from 500 to 1,000 louis a day.' They were not published, however, until 1899, in two volumes; Lord Rosebery called it 'the one capital and supreme record of life at St Helena', assuming that it was a private journal meant for the author's own eye.

Dr William Warden, who was naval surgeon in H.M.S. *Northumberland*, was the first to publish, in 1816; his *Letters* sold five editions in five months and was read with interest by Napoleon. General Bertrand's journal was published in French in 1821, but not translated (the first volume) into English until 1952, and the last volume not until 1960. Next came Dr Barry O'Meara, who left St Helena after a bitter quarrel with Sir Hudson Lowe, in August, 1818, and was dismissed from the Navy. He published his notorious *Napoleon in Exile; or a Voice from St. Helena*, in two volumes in 1822. It quickly ran into many editions and helped to ruin Sir Hudson Lowe. When Lowe returned to England after the death of

Napoleon, he was given for two years the command of troops in Ceylon, was then refused further employment and a pension, and died in poverty in 1844. O'Meara's medical diary was accepted as accurate at the time; but it has since been shown that the entries in the diary (written after his return to England) differ seriously from his daily reports as recorded in the original *Lowe Papers* in the British Museum.

Betsy Balcome (Mrs Abell) published her *Recollections* in 1845, and General Montholon's not very reliable *Récit* appeared in two volumes in 1847. Montchenu, Balmain and Stürmer, the Allied Commissioners, all told their stories of St Helena, though none of them ever actually met Napoleon; as did the Countess de Montholon, who knew him intimately (though not published until 1901), and Lady Malcolm, who related his conversations with her husband.

After the death of Napoleon in 1821 came the volumes by the doctors in attendance. Dr Alexander Arnott, who was surgeon to the 20th Regiment and only knew Napoleon during the last month of his life, published his *Account of the last illness etc. of Napoleon* in 1822. Dr Francesco Antommarchi, the young Corsican physician and anatomist who was sent to St Helena by Napoleon's family after the departure of Dr O'Meara, published his *Derniers moments de Napoléon* in two volumes in 1825; in the same year it was translated into English under the title *The Last Days of the Emperor Napoleon*. Lord Rosebery calls it 'worthless and mendacious', which is, however, an exaggeration, for it contains some undoubtedly valuable first-hand information. Dr Barry O'Meara's book has already been discussed, but probably the best book (even today, though Mr Kemble's recent book is much more detailed) on the medical aspects of the case is *The Illness and Death of Napoleon Bonaparte*, by Dr Arnold Chaplin, F.R.C.P., a well-known medical historian, who published his small volume in 1913. Dr Chaplin examined for the first time from the medical viewpoint the day to day record of the administration of Sir Hudson Lowe in the mass of *Lowe Papers* (134 volumes of them, 88 dealing with St Helena) available in the British Museum.

Sir Walter Scott's publisher, Constable, suggested a *Life of Napoleon Buonaparte* to him to help to pay his debts after his financial crash. He toiled at it prodigiously, acquired a hundred volumes of the official *Moniteur*, read innumerable books on the subject, and visited both Paris and London, where he had long conversations with the Duke of Wellington about Napoleon. The *Life*, most of which was written in twelve months, had as much matter in it as five of his novels. It was published in nine volumes in 1827, and its first two editions alone produced over £18,000 for his creditors.

Sir Walter complained that he had had to read over 300 books. He was fortunate in his day and age, for it has been calculated that 200,000 books about Napoleon have been written, and over 20,000 of his letters are in existence – his correspondence was published in 28 volumes in 1857–59 by order of Napoleon III, and many other letters have since come to light.

VI

During an unusually energetic mental and physical life, spent under active service conditions in diverse climates from Russia to Egypt, Napoleon had enjoyed uniform good health. He has been called an epileptic, but on tenuous evidence, for in his day 'epilepsy' and 'fits' were by no means precise terms, and the 'fits' were probably fits of temper, for which he was well known. It has been said that his unwonted lethargy at a critical moment that helped to lose the battle of Waterloo was due to an attack of piles (inflamed or thrombosed haemorrhoids), and it appears to be true that he was habitually constipated, requiring drastic remedies from time to time.

During the voyage to St Helena Napoleon did not have any occasion to consult Dr Warden, surgeon of H.M.S. *Northumberland*,

and when he landed on the island his health appeared to be excellent. Dr O'Meara, his personal surgeon, in his journal mentions merely a few occasions when Napoleon had 'headache and general uneasiness, which had been preceded by shiverings; had a little fever during the night', symptoms which sound like a cold or a mild influenza. He had already observed that Napoleon had habitually a slow pulse 'rarely exceeding 58 or 60 in a minute, and most frequently 54'.

On 1st October, 1817, however, Napoleon complained for the first time to Dr O'Meara that he had a dull pain and feeling of heaviness under the ribs on the right side and numbness and pain in the region of the right shoulder-blade. On 3rd October, O'Meara carried out a systematic examination of his patient, and noted that he 'examined the right side, and perceived that it felt firmer to the touch than the left. There was also a tumefaction evident to the sight, which when pressed hard gave a little pain. Napoleon said that this was observed about two months since. That he had thought nothing of it, and attributed it to obesity, but that now, from its being attended with pain, he imagined it might be connected with enlargement of the liver'.

From these signs and symptoms Dr O'Meara began to come to the conclusion that there might be some disorder of the liver, and mentioned the dire word 'hepatitis'. He prescribed calomel, anti-scorbutic vegetables, frictions, and hot sea-water baths. Political considerations were involved: the friends of Napoleon insisted that hepatitis was endemic in St Helena, that a high percentage of the troops constantly suffered from it, that it was due to the climate, and that the Emperor should be removed elsewhere. On the other hand, the British Government wished to emphasize that Napoleon was in the best of health and enjoying the 'bracing airs and salubrious climate' of St Helena. From this time until the end of his life Napoleon was apparently never quite free from a dull pain in his right side, sleeplessness, and depression, to which lack of exercise and increasing corpulence contributed.

On 16th November 1817, Dr O'Meara at last persuaded Napoleon to allow him to remove the carious and loose wisdom tooth which had been giving trouble for some months – and which was found among O'Meara's effects after his death and sold for seven and a half guineas.

Sir Hudson Lowe, the Governor, objected to Dr O'Meara using the word 'Emperor' to describe his patient in his official reports, but Napoleon would not allow him to use any other title. A compromise was arrived at by O'Meara making verbal reports to Dr Alexander Baxter, the Deputy Inspector of Hospitals, and he in turn made his reports to the Governor. During the next few months the difficulties between Dr O'Meara and the Governor increased and there were some violent scenes: O'Meara continued to emphasize the ill-health of Napoleon, but Dr Baxter made light of it in his reports. There is little doubt that the ill-feeling between O'Meara and Sir Hudson Lowe coloured his medical opinions, while Baxter was a personal friend of the Governor's and naturally took his side. Dr O'Meara was barred from the officers' mess by command of the Governor, and finally, with the approval of the Secretary at War, he was dismissed from Longwood and sent back to England on 2nd August 1818. In a report to the Admiralty he virtually accused Hudson Lowe of inciting him to accelerate the death of Napoleon, and his name was officially 'erased from the list of naval surgeons'.

After the departure of Dr O'Meara the Governor appointed Dr Verling, assistant surgeon to the Royal Artillery, resident physician at Longwood; but although he took up his residence there, Napoleon refused to see him, so that Verling never actually attended him. Little is known about Napoleon's health between July 1818, and September 1819, except that he more and more frequently lay, sometimes for hours, in hot baths, to which he had long been addicted as a luxury rather than a necessity.

On 17th January 1819, Napoleon had a severe attack of vertigo and lost consciousness. By permission of the Governor, Dr John Stockoe, surgeon to H.M.S. *Conqueror*, was allowed to be called in by the household, in place of Verling. Dr Stockoe had been friendly with Dr O'Meara and had once met Napoleon, with whom he was able to converse in Italian. He found his patient still complaining of the pain in the right side, under the ribs, shooting up to the right shoulder. A warm bath brought relief, although headache and giddiness continued, and Stockoe recommended a slight degree of bleeding and a saline purgative. He 'detected a degree of hardness' in the liver and, following O'Meara, diagnosed 'hepatitis'. This contravened the official policy and Dr Stockoe was not allowed to continue his professional attendance. He was, in fact, later court-martialled and dismissed from the service.

VII

Meanwhile representations had been made to the British Government about the medical care of Napoleon, and his family were allowed to send out to St Helena a personal physician and two priests. The physician, chosen by Cardinal Fesch, Madame Mère's half-brother, was a young Corsican, Dr Francesco Antommarchi, aged 30, who had qualified in medicine at the university of Pisa and had become prosector (i.e. the assistant who prepared bodies for dissection) to the professor of anatomy at Florence; but his knowledge of medical practice was but small. One of the priests, Abbé Buonavita, was old and crippled by a stroke – he had been chaplain to Madame Mère at Elba; and the other, Abbé Vignali, was young, a country lad from Corsica without much education, to whom, however, Napoleon took a liking. Two new and not very efficient servants accompanied them. It has been suggested that the reason for such a curious selection was because a clairvoyant had assured Madame Mère that Napoleon was no longer at St Helena, but had been transported far away to a hiding-place.

Dr Antommarchi was interviewed at the Colonial Office in London and told that the previous medical reports should be discounted and that Napoleon was in fact very well. He arrived at St Helena on 20th September 1819, and remained in attendance upon Napoleon to the end. He published in 1825, in Paris and London, his

Derniers moments de Napoléon, in which he described fully the progress of Napoleon's last illness. Dr Arnold Chaplin wrote, 'Antommarchi's book is highly tinctured with romance and without corroboration is of very little value'. Nevertheless, he was an import-ant eye-witness, and his story, when it is corroborated, gives a vivid picture of the last days of Napoleon.

He examined his patient for the first time on 23rd September 1819 and found him with a pulse-rate of 60 (unusually high for Napoleon) and a coated tongue. He complained of constant pain on the right side, in the right shoulder and the right breast. He had a dry cough, and from time to time had nausea and vomiting. On examination, he found the region over the left lobe of the liver hard and painful to the touch. He prescribed exercise, a calming potion, hot baths, and a liniment composed of opium and ammonia.

Napoleon was persuaded, with some difficulty, of the value of exercise, and by the end of October 1819, he was out of doors almost every day and had taken up gardening with enthusiasm. The benefit to his health was soon evident, and he began to eat and sleep well and lost his depression. By May, 1820, he felt so well that he re-sumed riding on horseback, the limits previously assigned to him having been relaxed. But in July 1820, his old troubles began to reappear, pain, occasional vomiting, cough, sweating, constipation, sometimes fever and a quick pulse, sometimes fits of lethargy. On 4th October he had his last ride on horseback, his health began to fail, and he began to walk slowly about Longwood holding on to the arm of one of his suite.

Napoleon protested that since Dr Antommarchi was unable to make a precise diagnosis of his disease, the drugs prescribed were inappropriate. But, on the whole, the remedies suggested were suitable enough, except for the tartar emetic administered on 22nd, 23rd and 24th March 1821, which – with a severely ulcerated stomach – naturally caused abundant vomiting.

On 25th March Antommarchi thought it advisable to have a consultation with Dr Archibald Arnott, surgeon to the 20th

Regiment, and at the time senior medical officer on the island. Dr
Arnott did not at first see the patient, but on hearing Antommarchi's account of the illness advised purgatives, a blister to the
stomach, and saline draughts. Napoleon got worse, and on 1st
April Arnott examined Napoleon, though it is evident from his
reports that he did not at first understand the seriousness of the
illness. In 1822 Dr Arnott published *An Account of the Last Illness
of Napoleon*, from which it seemed evident that the physician
understood completely the serious nature of the case. But it was
written after the death of Napoleon and with knowledge of the
post-mortem examination. The day-to-day reports by Arnott, in the
Lowe Papers in the British Museum, tell a very different story. On
22nd April 1821, he was assuring the Governor that the disease was
merely hypochondriasis, there was no danger, and that 'the cure
would be tedious owing to the fact that the patient could not be
given the thing he most desired, liberty'. Vomiting became incessant, pain and distension of the abdomen were severe, and rigors
frequent. Weakness progressively became more marked, Napoleon
became comatose, and died on the evening of 5th May 1821, at the
age of 51.

VIII

A post-mortem examination was carried out on the afternoon of
6th May, by Dr Antommarchi, in the presence of Dr Thomas
Shortt, Principal Medical Officer; Dr Archibald Arnott, Surgeon
to the 20th Regiment; Dr Francis Burton, Surgeon to the 66th
Regiment; Dr Matthew Livingstone, Surgeon to the East India
Company; Dr Charles Mitchell, Surgeon of H.M.S. *Vigo*; Dr
George Henry Rutledge, Assistant Surgeon to the 20th Regiment;
and Dr Walter Henry, Assistant Surgeon to the 66th Regiment.

There were also present Count Bertrand and General Montholon,
Sir Thomas Reade, Deputy Adjutant-General to the Governor,
Major Charles Harrison, and Captain William Crokat, the Duty
Officer at Longwood. The Abbé Vignali, St Denis, the Emperor's

valet, and Pieron, his butler, made a total of 17 persons. The Frenchmen present were waiting anxiously to see an incision made into the liver to prove the presence of an abscess. The Englishmen must have given up their hypothesis of hypochondriasis, but were equally ignorant of the cause of death.

Three accounts of the post-mortem examination are extant: an official one signed by Dr Shortt and his four senior colleagues; one by Dr Antommarchi on behalf of the French representatives; and an 'unofficial' one (in the *Lowe Papers*) written by Dr Henry from notes made at the time.

The official post-mortem report states: 'A trifling adhesion of the left pleura to the pleura costalis was found; about three ounces of reddish fluid were contained in the left cavity, and nearly eight ounces in the right. The lungs were quite sound. The pericardium was natural, and contained about an ounce of fluid. The heart was of the natural size, but thickly covered with fat; the auricles and ventricles exhibited nothing extraordinary, except that the muscular parts appeared rather paler than natural.

'Upon opening the abdomen, the omentum was found remarkably fat, and on exposing the stomach that viscus was found the seat of extensive disease; strong adhesions connected the whole superior surface, particularly about the pyloric extremity, to the concave surface of the left lobe of the liver; and on separating these, an ulcer which penetrated the coats of the stomach was discovered one inch from the pylorus, sufficient to allow the passage of the little finger. The internal surface of the stomach to nearly its whole extent was a mass of cancerous disease, or scirrhous portions advancing to cancer; this was particularly noticed near the pylorus. The cardiac extremity for a small space near the termination of the oesophagus, was the only part appearing in a healthy state. The stomach was found nearly filled with a large quantity of fluid, resembling coffee grounds.

'The convex surface of the left lobe of the liver adhered to the diaphragm, but with the exception of the adhesions occasioned by the disease in the stomach, no unhealthy appearance presented itself in the liver. The remainder of the abdominal viscera were in a healthy state. A slight peculiarity in the formation of the left kidney was observed.

(Signed) SHORTT, ARNOTT, BURTON,
LIVINGSTONE, MITCHELL.'

Dr Henry's account is in the *Lowe Papers*, in the form of a letter to Sir Hudson Lowe. The important part of it runs as follows: 'On exposing the contents of the abdomen, the omentum was seen loaded with fat of which the quantity was very great. When the stomach was brought into view, an adhesion of great extent was perceived between its superior surface and the concave surface of the left lobe of the liver. On separating them, which was a matter of a very considerable difficulty, the fatal disease at once developed its seat and extent. The whole internal superficies of the stomach exhibited the appearance of a mass of cancerous ulceration, or scirrhous thickening fast advancing to cancer. It was cut out and carefully examined. The pylorus was the focus of the disorganisation, where the disease had quite eroded the substance of the stomach, and a hole was formed through which the writer put his finger. This was stopped up by the adhesions to the part of the liver immediately contiguous, otherwise death must have taken place when the stomach was first penetrated. There were no indications of any injury having been sustained by the liver from contact with the various fluids passing through the alimentary canal. A ring surrounding the cardiac extremity immediately adjoining the entrance of the oesophagus was the only portion of the organ which appeared capable of discharging its important functions. It was filled with dark-coloured fluid resembling the grounds of coffee.

'A very general expectation was entertained that the liver would be found in a diseased state, the illness of the deceased having been so confidently referred to an enlargement of the liver and chronic inflammation of this viscus. In consequence when the liver was next examined, the countenances of the spectators indicated much anxiety. When M. Antommarchi made his first incision into it, he expected to see a flow of pus from the abscess which had been anticipated in its substance, but no abscess, no hardness, no enlargement, no inflammation were observed. On the contrary, the liver was of natural size, and perfectly healthy in its internal parts. There was a small adhesion of the convex surface of the left lobe to the diaphragm, which appeared to have been a continuation and a consequence of the adjoining adhesions between the liver and the stomach.

'The gall bladder was of proper size and structure, containing no gall stones, but the usual quantity of apparently healthy bile. The spleen, pancreas, and intestines were sound. The kidneys were embedded in an immense quantity of fat. The left kidney was one-third larger than the right, this enlargement appeared to have been congenital.'

The other extant account of the post-mortem examination is that of Dr Antommarchi, on behalf of the French representatives. After giving an account of the measurements of the body and its external appearances, he reported as follows:

'The left lung was slightly compressed by effusion, and adhered by numerous threads to the posterior and lateral parts of the chest and to the pericardium. I dissected it with care, and found the superior lobe sprinkled with tubercles and some small tuberculous excavations.

'The right lung was slightly compressed by effusion, but its parenchyma was in a normal state. Generally speaking both lungs were crepitant and of a natural colour.

'Many of the glands of the bronchi and of the mediastinum were a little enlarged, almost degenerated, and in a state of suppuration.

'The pericardium was in a healthy condition and contained about an ounce of fluid of a citron colour. The heart which was a little larger than the fist of the subject exhibited, although sound, a more than usual amount of fat at its base and on its ridges. The ventricles and auricles were healthy, but pale and quite empty. The orifices did not show any notable lesion. The great arterial and venous vessels near the heart were empty, but generally in a sound condition.

'A soft, transparent, and diffluent exudation lined the whole extent of the contiguous parts of the internal surface of the peritoneum.

'The spleen and the liver which was hardened were very large and distended with blood. The tissue of the liver, which was reddy brown in colour, did not, however, present any other notable alteration in structure. Extremely clotted and thick bile filled and distended the gall bladder. The liver, which was affected with chronic hepatitis, was closely united by its convex surface to the diaphragm; the adhesion extended over the whole organ and was strong, cellular, and of long standing. The concave surface of the left lobe of the liver adhered closely and firmly to the corresponding part of the stomach, especially along the small curve of that organ, and also to the little epiploon. At every point of contact the lobe was sensibly thickened, swollen, and hardened.

'The stomach appeared at first to be in a most healthy state, with no trace of irritation or phlogosis, and the peritoneal membrane presented the most satisfactory appearance. But on examining the organ with care, I discovered on the anterior surface, towards the small curve, and three fingers' breadth from the pylorus, a slight obstruction of a scirrhous nature, of very small extent and exactly circumscribed. The stomach was pierced through and through in the centre of this small induration. The adhesion between this part of the stomach and the left lobe of the liver closed up this perforation.

'On opening this viscus along its great curve, I observed that a part of its cavity was filled with a considerable quantity of matters slightly consistent, and mixed with much glareous substance, very thick, and of a colour similar to that of "coffee grounds", which exhaled an acrid and offensive odour. These matters being taken away, the mucous membrane of the stomach was found to be in a healthy state, from the small to the large ending of that viscus along the great curve. Almost all the rest of the internal surface of the organ was occupied by a cancerous ulcer which had its centre at the superior part along the small curve of the stomach, while the irregular, digital and linguiform edges of its circumference extended before and behind this internal surface from the orifice of the cardiac end to within a good inch of the pylorus. The rounded perforation, cut obliquely on the bevel at the expense of the internal surface of the viscus, occupied scarcely four or five lines in diameter inside, and at most two and a half lines outside. The circular border of the external opening was extremely thin, slightly denticulated, and blackish, and was formed only by the peritoneal membrane of the stomach. An ulcerous, greyish, and smooth surface lined the walls of this kind of canal which would have established a communication between the cavity of the stomach and that of the abdomen, if the adhesion between the liver and the stomach had not prevented it. The right extremity of the stomach, an inch away from the pylorus, was surrounded by a swelling, or rather an annular scirrhous hardening, of some lines in breadth. The orifice of the pylorus was in a perfectly natural state. The edges of the ulcer exhibited remarkable fungous swellings, the bases of which were hard, thick, and in a scirrhous state, and extended as well to the whole surface occupied by that cruel disease.

'The little epiploon was contracted, swollen, extremely hard, and degenerated. The lymphatic glands of this peritoneal covering, those which are placed along the curves of the stomach, and those which are around the pillars of the diaphragm, were in part tumefied and scirrhous, and some even in a state of suppuration.

'The digestive canal was distended by a large quantity of gas. I observed on the peritoneal surface and in its folds small spots and patches of a very light red colour, of various sizes, and disseminated. The mucous membrane of the digestive canal appeared to be in a healthy state. A blackish and extremely viscous substance lined the large intestine.

'The right kidney was healthy; the left, displaced and thrown back across the lumbar vertebral column, was longer and narrower than the other, but seemed to be sound. The bladder, empty and very contracted, contained a certain amount of gravel mixed with definite small calculi. Numerous red patches were scattered over the mucous membrane of this organ, and its walls were in a diseased state.'

There is no doubt that death was due to cancer of the lesser curvature of the stomach, probably originating in a chronic gastric ulcer, and that this had penetrated as far as the liver, to which it was adherent. The lymphatic glands of the omentum were enlarged, but there were apparently no secondary growths elsewhere. The liver was stated to be 'large', but there was no real evidence of hepatitis (though Antommarchi mentioned it) or other liver disease.

Two specimens were for many years preserved in the Museum of the Royal College of Surgeons in London, described in the catalogue as 'Incipient Fungous in the Glands of the Intestines, Napoleon; Barry O'Meara to Sir Astley Cooper'. They were destroyed (with much besides) in May 1941, but in any case their genuineness had long been doubted, though that careful anatomist Sir Arthur Keith, who was curator of the Museum, accepted them as genuine. He was influenced because of his belief in Sir Astley Cooper and 'when he attached the brief label to the Napoleonic relics we may be certain that he knew how O'Meara obtained them.' Apparently Antommarchi met O'Meara in London and discussed Napoleon's illness with him. Sir Astley Cooper pronounced the specimens to be cancerous growths, but modern and more accurate methods of examination showed them to be chronic inflammation of Peyer's (lymphoid) patches in the intestinal wall, which may help to support the diagnosis of a tropical infection. Barry O'Meara left St Helena in 1818, three years before the death of Napoleon, and it would have been impossible to have removed part of the intestine under the eyes of seventeen witnesses; the heart was put into a silver vase and the stomach into a silver pepper-box before being placed in the coffin along with the body, of which Dr Rutledge was instructed to take charge, with strict orders to allow nothing to be removed.

The recent suggestion that Napoleon died of arsenical poisoning – indeed, the word 'murdered' was used – was founded on the examination in the Department of Forensic Medicine at Glasgow of a tuft of hairs said to have come from the head of Napoleon; his head was shaved after death and so provided many such souvenirs. By a new activation test the hair was found to have an arsenical content of 10·38 p.p.m., compared with a normal 0·8 p.p.m. A second specimen of longer hairs was provided by M. Frey, a Swiss textile manufacturer, who had read about the first; they were a family heirloom, contained in an envelope on which was a note about them signed by J. A. Noverraz, Napoleon's valet at St Helena. They also were found to contain arsenic, which did not occur evenly throughout the hair and was not present in the part farthest from the skull. It is true that severe gastritis (and even hepatitis) can be caused by poisonous doses of arsenic; but arsenious oxide was formerly in common use in medicine, prescribed (in small doses) as a 'gastric stimulant' and also (in larger doses) for anaemia, malaria, arthritis, and skin conditions such as psoriasis. It may well have been employed in treatment and certainly was no more unlikely or more drastic than the tartar emetic and the ten grains of calomel undoubtedly prescribed by Dr Antommarchi. The three post-mortem reports, however, contain conclusive evidence that death was due to cancer of the stomach.

REFERENCES

SIR HUDSON LOWE. *The Lowe Papers*, British Museum, Additional Manuscripts Nos. 20107–20240. 1816 onwards.

BARRY E. O'MEARA. *Napoleon in Exile; or, A Voice from St. Helena*, 2 vols. Simpkin & Marshall, London 1822.

COUNT DE LAS CASES. *Journal of the Private Life of Napoleon at St. Helena*, 5 vols. Colburn, London 1823.

C. F. ANTOMMARCHI. *The Last Days of the Emperor Napoleon*, Colburn, London 1825.

REAR-ADMIRAL SIR F. L. MAITLAND. *Narrative of the Surrender of Napoleon*, Colburn, London 1826.

SIR WALTER SCOTT. *Life of Napoleon Buonaparte*, 9 vols. Longman, London, and Cadell, Edinburgh 1827.

LOUIS BONAPARTE (ex-King of Holland). *A Reply to Sir Walter Scott's History of Napoleon*, Translated from the French. Hurst & Co, London 1829.

Mémoires de Napoléon. (By the generals who shared his captivity.) Bossange Pére, Paris 1830.

MRS ABELL. *Recollections of Napoleon at St Helena*, John Murray, London 1845.

W. FORSYTH. *History of the Captivity of Napoleon at St Helena*, 3 vols. John Murray, London 1853.

LORD ROSEBERY. *Napoleon: the Last Phase*, Humphreys, London 1900.

ARNOLD CHAPLIN. *The Illness and Death of Napoleon Bonaparte*, Hirschfeld, London 1913.

SIR ARTHUR KEITH. *British Medical Journal*, 1913, Vol. *i*, page 53.

JULIAN PARK (trans. and edited by). *Napoleon in Captivity* (by Count Balmain). Allen & Unwin, London 1928.

JAMES KEMBLE. *Napoleon Immortal*, John Murray, London 1959.

RALPH KORNGOLD. *The Last Years of Napoleon*, Gollancz, London 1960.

STEN FORSHUFVUD, HAMILTON SMITH and ANDERS WASSÉN. *Arsenic content of Napoleon I's hair*. Nature, 14th Oct., 1961, Vol. **192**, p. 103.

idem: Distribution of arsenic in Napoleon's hair. Nature, 26th May 1962, Vol. **194**, p. 725

STEN FORSHUFVUD. *Who killed Napoleon?* Trans. by Alan Brodrick, Hutchinson, London 1962.

CHAPTER X

THE INSANITY OF KING GEORGE III

KING GEORGE III reigned for a longer period than any other English monarch with the exception of Queen Victoria. He was born in 1738, the son of Frederick, Prince of Wales, and succeeded his grandfather, King George II, in 1760, his father having died when he was 13. King George II had been subject to fits of depression, his absurd son Frederick – 'Poor Fred' – was, in the Hanoverian tradition, always at loggerheads with him, and King George III's mother was 'a foolish, ignorant woman' with a history of feeble-mindedness in her family. George III, the first of the Hanoverian kings to speak English as his native tongue, was educated by a succession of tutors, one or two of them highly unsuitable, and his education was constantly the subject of political controversy. In 1761 he married Princess Charlotte of Mecklenburg and settled down to a life of homely domesticity, though disturbed in later years by wars and political controversies and by the misbehaviour of his heir George, Prince of Wales (afterwards King George IV). He had good taste in music and was a patron of science and the arts, though he preferred Benjamin West to Joshua Reynolds.

He was not at first popular with the general public, contributed to by his partiality for the unpopular Scotsman, Lord Bute. The first strong public demonstration of affection came in 1789 after his recovery from his serious mental illness, partly out of sympathy and partly in indignation at the callous behaviour of his son and his Whig friends. His determination to fight on against the French increased his popularity, as did his friendly habit of gossiping with country folk and even his puzzle of how the apples got into the dumplings, and 'Farmer George' held the affection of his people up to the end of his long life, in spite of his mental aberrations. As the historian Bisset wrote: 'He was punctually assiduous in the exercise of his royal functions, exemplary in the fulfilment of all the social duties, affable yet dignified in his deportment toward his subjects, and in works of charity unostentatiously munificent.'

Early in his reign King George III obtained control of his Government and his Ministers took their orders direct from him. In 1780, however, Dunning's motion that 'The power of the Crown has increased, is increasing, and ought to be diminished' was passed by the House of Commons, and during William Pitt's long ministry the power of a strong Prime Minister kept increasing and he and his Cabinet became more and more independent of the Crown. Although Pitt and other Ministers showed themselves unwilling to oppose strongly-held prejudices of the King, such as against Catholic emancipation, this was not because of political weakness but because of the possibility of inducing another attack of insanity. During the reign of his successor, King George IV, the constitutional victory of Prime Minister and Cabinet was consolidated.

Much of our intimate knowledge of King George III and his Queen is obtainable in the diary of Fanny Burney (afterwards Madame D'Arblay) the novelist, author of *Evelina* and the 'petted' friend of Dr Johnson. Through another friend, Mrs Delany, an aristocratic widow of literary tastes, she was appointed to the salaried post of 'second keeper of the robes' to Queen Charlotte, with whom she lived on terms of close intimacy. She remained in the royal service from 1785 to 1791, and then married a French exile, Alexandre D'Arblay, an artillery officer who became a general. Her diary extended from 1768 over 72 years.

II

As early as the spring of 1765 King George III showed signs of mental disorder, though this attack was kept so secret by the Court as apparently not to have been suspected even by the Prime Minister. To the world it was given out that the King's illness at this time was a cough and fever; that he had caught cold in coming out of the House of Lords; and lastly that 'owing to the unskilfulness of his physicians, a humour, which ought to have appeared in his face, had settled upon his chest'. Fortunately the King made a quick recovery, and the truth about the state of his health at this time was not realized until his later recurrent aberrations made it clear.

III

In June 1788, the King, having had what he called 'a smart bilious attack', was recommended by Sir George Baker, M.D. to go for a month to Cheltenham, to take the waters there. Sir George Baker was Physician-in-Ordinary to the King, President of the College of Physicians in 1798, and a classical scholar, to whom Gray dedicated his 'Elegy written in a Country Churchyard'. When the King returned to Windsor he was apparently in good health, but in October, 'having been slightly indisposed' he went for a walk for four hours in the rain and next day was attacked by 'spasms in the stomach', becoming so ill as to alarm the royal household.

It is interesting that the first person not connected with the Royal Family who seems to have entertained a suspicion of incipient insanity was the celebrated actress Mrs Siddons, a great favourite of King George III and his Queen, whom she entertained with Shakespearean recitals and readings. During a visit to Windsor Castle the King, without any apparent motive, placed in her hands a sheet of paper, blank except for his signature, which struck her as so unaccountable that she immediately carried it to the Queen, who thanked her for her discretion. A few days later the truth of the King's illness forced itself upon Sir George Baker, who communicated his fears to the Ministry. In order to avoid creating any unnecessary alarm, it was determined, however, that the King should appear at a levée which had been arranged, but there the King's disordered dress and garrulous mode of talking caused many uneasy observations. Lord Chancellor Thurlow advised the King that as he was looking ill he should return to Windsor and look after himself, to which the King replied excitedly 'Born a gentleman, I shall never lay my head on my last pillow in peace and quiet so long as I remember the loss of my American Colonies!' He removed, however, with his family to Windsor where, according to Miss Burney, 'his manner was gracious almost to kindness, but, on the other hand, the hoarseness of his voice, the volubility of his language, and the vehemence of his gestures, startled her beyond measure'.

His physicians found him a refractory patient – day after day he spent as long as five hours on horseback, though once, on returning from a ride he burst into tears and exclaimed to the Duke of York that 'he wished to God he might die, for he was going to be mad'. At dinner with his family the King was suddenly seized with delirium; he caught hold of the Prince of Wales by the collar, pushing him against the wall with some violence, and asked him who would dare say to the King of England that he should not speak out, or who should prevent his whispering. The King then whispered.

At six o'clock on the following morning Miss Burney went to the Queen's apartment, where she found her royal mistress sitting up in bed, wan and colourless. Only too audibly, issuing from the adjoining apartment, were overheard the hoarse voice and incessant loquacity of the afflicted monarch. The Lord Chancellor, at the express summons of the Prince of Wales, proceeded to Windsor Castle, where he received from the three physicians who were in attendance – Dr Warren, Dr Heberden, and Sir George Baker – a most distressing and alarming account of the King's condition. They were not only of opinion, they said, that the King's life was in imminent danger, but that, in the event of his recovery, loss of reason was greatly to be apprehended. 'The alternative,' wrote William Grenville, 'is one to which one cannot look without horror – that of a continuance of the present derangement of his faculties,

without any other effect upon his health.' One of the most remarkable features of the King's mental disorder was his never-ceasing
garrulity. On one occasion he is said to have talked unceasingly for
sixteen hours, and talked 'of everybody and everything'.

It has recently been suggested that Dr. Warren was a mere
stooge of the Prince of Wales, anxious to please his patron by
declaring the King's mental disorder incurable. But on the contrary
Dr Richard Warren, though perhaps old-fashioned in his approach
to a case of insanity, was one of the best physicians in London,
Physician-in-Ordinary to the King since 1763, Harveian Lecturer
and three times Censor to the College of Physicians, physician to
the Middlesex Hospital and then to St. George's Hospital, "One
of the few great characters of his time whose popularity was not
the fruit of party favour".

The Prince of Wales, the Duke of York, and the physicians and
equerries were sitting up at night on sofas and chairs in an apartment close to the King's, when he suddenly appeared among
them, recognized Sir George Baker and held him against the wall,
telling him that he had mistaken his complaint, which was only
nervousness, and that he was nothing more or less than an old
woman. Public sympathy was on the side of the afflicted King,
and the King's physicians began to receive anonymous letters
threatening them with condign punishment if the illness proved
fatal.

The opposition Whigs, led by Fox, Burke and Sheridan, saw
the opportunity of supplanting Pitt and his Ministry if the King's
physicians were to declare his insanity incurable, and if the Prince
of Wales, their patron, were then appointed Regent, with full
powers of patronage, appointing Ministers, making peers and
granting pensions. It had in fact become the unkind habit at cards
at Brooks's Club, their headquarters, to call out "the lunatic"
instead of "the king".

Parliament assembled on 4th December 1788, when Mr Pitt in
the House of Commons and Lord Camden in the House of Lords

laid upon the tables of the two Houses the evidence of the royal physicians who, on the preceding day, had been examined before the Privy Council as to the state of the King's health. Generally speaking, their opinions were in favour of ultimate recovery. It was Pitt's recommendation that the care and management of the King's person should be vested in the Queen; and at the same time he proposed to confer on the Prince of Wales the office of Regent, but with restricted powers.

The physicians had pointed out that the distance of Windsor from London occasioned them great personal inconvenience, and that exercise in the open air was necessary for the King's well being, and therefore proposed his removal from Windsor to Kew Palace, where he was under the care of trained attendants rather than equerries or pages. Happily Dr Francis Willis was now called in by the Queen (on 5th December 1788), and the available evidence goes to show that he treated the King with more humanity than was generally accorded to lunatics in those days.

Dr Francis Willis is remembered in history only because of his connexion with King George III, but he was also an interesting and unusual character. He was born in 1718, the son of a vicar of Lincoln Cathedral, and educated at Oxford, where he became a Fellow (and vice-principal) of Brasenose College. He took holy orders in 1740, and became vicar of Gretford, near Stamford, where he kept a private madhouse; later on, he was also rector of Wapping. To stifle criticism, Willis obtained the degree of doctor of medicine from Oxford University in 1779. The Archbishop of Canterbury said of him: 'Since Dr Willis of Lincolnshire has been called in, our hope has been more firm and constant, and at this moment stands very high. He has had great experience in this malady for eight-and-twenty years, and great success.' He was assisted by his son, Dr John.

When he was first introduced at Court the King expressed surprise at a clergyman practising medicine, to which Willis rejoined that the Saviour Himself had cured demoniacs. 'Yes,' said the

King, in one of his more lucid moments, 'but he did not get £700 a year for it, heh?'

Willis's treatment consisted in the administration of Peruvian bark (i.e. quinine), blistering, and an occasional dose of calomel, though when the King became maniacal Willis did not hesitate to have him confined in a strait-jacket. He adopted at times a liberality of treatment which astonished and terrified his more nervous medical colleagues. He not only allowed the King a pen-knife with which to cut his nails, but even permitted him to shave himself. He was sure, said Dr Willis to the King, as he presented the razor to him, that His Majesty was too good a Christian, and had too much sense of what he owed to his people, to attempt self-destruction. Of all the physicians, Dr Willis was the most sanguine about the King's recovery.

In February 1789, the King's malady began to take a favourable turn, and he said to Dr Willis, 'Willis, you do not know your own business. You ought to accustom me to see people by degrees, that I may be prepared for seeing them more at large.' On 14th February Miss Burney records that the King and Queen were walking arm in arm in Richmond Gardens, and the bulletin on 17th February proclaimed His Majesty to be in a state of convalescence. On 20th February the Lord Chancellor was able to report to Pitt 'that he never saw, at any period, the King more composed, collected, or distinct, and that there was not the least trace or appearance of disorder'.

After the restoration to health of the King, Dr Francis Willis was granted an annuity of £1,500 a year for twenty-one years, while his son John, who was also in attendance, got a pension of £550 for life, to which were added fees of 30 guineas for each visit to Windsor and 10 guineas for each visit to Kew. In the case of Sir George Baker, who was longest in attendance, the fees amounted to 1,300 guineas. The reputation that Willis gained by his treatment of King George III led to his being called to the mentally disordered Queen of Portugal. She had the delusion that she was in hell, and said that a physician might sometimes cure madness but could never reverse the decrees of fate. For his services to her Willis received £20,000. He died in 1807.

On 10th March, the day on which the physicians took their departure from Kew, there was exhibited at night 'the most magnificent illumination that perhaps ever lighted up the capital of England', and the blaze extended to Greenwich, Hampstead, and Brentford. 'The nation,' according to Lord Macaulay, 'was wild with delight'; and, wrote Miss Burney, 'All Windsor came out to meet the King. It was a joy amounting to ecstasy.'

IV

King George III remained well until February 1801, when mental derangement returned, apparently in consequence of Pitt's agitation in favour of the Catholic Relief Bill, for it was their Protestantism that had placed the Hanoverian kings on the English throne. It began with a cold so severe that the King could scarcely speak, treated with James's powder (a mixture of antimonious oxide and calcium phosphates, with a diaphoretic action). Although the disorder was not of an alarming character, it contained the seeds of the same malady that prostrated him in 1788 and 1789. In consequence of the King's complaining of lack of sleep, he was persuaded by Addington, then Prime Minister, whose father was a physician (hence his celebrated nickname of 'the doctor') to use a pillow filled with hops.

On 21st February the King was in a high fever, and the services of the younger Dr Willis were imperatively required (the elder Dr Willis was not summoned until 25th February). By 2nd March, however, the King's pulse-rate was reduced from 136 per minute to 84, and by 4th March he had apparently recovered. On 6th March Dr John Willis wrote to Mr Pitt: 'Her Majesty and the Dukes of Kent and Cumberland went in to the King at half after five o'clock, and remained with him for two hours. They came out

L

perfectly satisfied; in short, everything that passed has confirmed all that you heard we say today. He has desired to see the Duke of York tomorrow, and all the Princesses in their turn.'

V

Towards the middle of January 1804, the King was again seized with an attack of illness, which before long was followed by a temporary mental derangement. The Lord Chancellor reported that he walked with the King two or three times round Buckingham House gardens, without the slightest aberration in his Majesty's conversation, but when they returned to the House, the King, laying down his hat and cane, placed his head upon the Lord Chancellor's shoulder and burst into tears.

On 14th February the King talked for five hours incessantly, on the 15th, 'his mind was much affected, but his animal functions not deranged'. On the 17th, 'the King had foreseen his illness coming on, and had made arrangements in case of his death. For a short time he suffered a sort of paralysis which created great apprehensions for his life; but there soon appeared no ground for that alarm. The disorder has now taken the decided character of a complete mental derangement'.

The King had conceived a morbid horror of being attended by any member of the Willis family, accordingly, at his urgent desire, Dr Samuel Foart Simmons, physician to St Luke's Hospital (rival institution to the old foundation of Bethlem), was called in. Dr Simmons said that 'relapses in this disorder were frequent, and many persons returned to St Luke's at intervals, but that the attack was always slighter upon each successive fit'.

So satisfactory was the progress of the King that on 27th February 1804, the physicians were able to intimate to the Cabinet that, 'though it was still advisable that his Majesty should avoid fatiguing arguments and discussions, yet he was perfectly competent to perform any act of government'.

VI

The final attack of insanity of King George III was precipitated by the painful and lingering illness of his favourite daughter, Princess Amelia. On 24th October 1810, the King's excited manner and loud and rapid utterance gave the first warning of a return of the mental derangement which had afflicted him on former occasions.

The Willises had excited the anger of the Prince of Wales and also that of the Queen, by not allowing free access to the King. When this new attack came on the royal family at once thought of sending for Dr John Willis and the Chancellor came to him to say that it was necessary that he should attend. The other firmly refused, alleging the dislike with which he was regarded at Court. Accordingly he was surprised one morning to see the carriage of the Regent drive up, when the Prince came in and invited himself to breakfast. Putting on his most seductive manner he told Willis that he had been angry because the last time the King was under his charge he had been staggered by seeing a board with the words printed on it in large letters: 'No one to pass this way without permission from John Willis, M.D.' But he now understood from the Chancellor that this was never intended to apply to himself or his brother.

The result was that Dr John Willis proceeded once more to Windsor to the King's old quarters. He was ascending the stairs when he heard the sound of singing and whistling, and presently the figure of the King was seen arrayed in the blue coat, star, cocked hat and top-boots, so familiar from pictures all over the kingdom. He had a whip, with which he was switching his boots carelessly. At the sight of the doctor he gave a piteous shriek: 'Oh! John Willis again! God help me!' and fell on the ground in a fit.

There can be no doubt that the King's condition could be described as that of insanity, with occasional lucid intervals, rather than, as his family and his Ministers tried to represent it, that of sanity with occasional relapses into insanity. The Queen and the Court had begun by trying to conceal the illness. The confusion and embarrassment caused by the King's malady may well be imagined, and each political party, helped by the experience of twenty years before, determined to take every advantage that was offered.

Mr Perceval (the Prime Minister) had no intention of leaving the powers of the Prince of Wales unfettered, and the following restrictions were made: 1. From making peers. 2. Granting offices in reversion or pensions. 3. The King's property to lie in trustees. 4. The care of the King to be entrusted to the Queen and a Council.

VII

An almost day-to-day commentary is to be found in the correspondence of Mr W. H. Fremantle, M.P., who lived at Englefield Green, near Windsor, with the Marquis, afterwards Duke, of Buckingham. The intimate details given sound as if he must have been in close touch with one at least of the King's physicians. Fremantle writes as follows:

October 31, 1810. 'For some time before the physicians were called upon to attend him, he had shown evident symptoms of the disorder; but, for the last two or three days, he has been gradually getting worse, and the strongest medical discipline which he has undergone, has not removed or lessened the irritation.'

November 1, 1810. 'The King continues as bad as ever. The irritation has never ceased since Tuesday and has gradually increased; he is quite ungovernable, but as yet nobody has been called in as a medical adviser but Halford, Baillie, Heberden, and Dundas. Unless the mind is more subdued tomorrow, further advice will be thought necessary, and of persons (i.e. the Willises) who have before been consulted upon his malady. The worst symptom is the great and increasing agitation of mind, without the accompaniment of fever. He talks incessantly, and, in short, has exactly every symptom which you have before seen detailed in the reports of his former attacks.

'The Chancellor and Lord Wellesley came to Windsor today,

to examine the physicians. Three questions were put by them: *First*. Is the King capable of signing his name to any instrument? *Answer*. The King is at this moment incapable. *Second*. What has in your opinion caused the King's illness? *Answer*. The unfortunate state of the Princess Amelia, which has agitated his mind. *Third*. Do you think the King likely to recover? *Answer*. We have known many instances of recovery in similar cases.'

November 2, 1810. 'The King is worse today – nothing can be more dreadful than his situation for the last three days – he is quite ungovernable. Yesterday, at six o'clock, an express was sent for Simmons's people. He came down at once, accompanied by his son and four assistants. He desired to have the sole management of the King, without which he could do nothing. This was refused him by the physicians, in consequence of which, he went back with his troop immediately. Heberden went this morning in search of somebody else, and it is supposed Willis's people. The object is for the physicians to control and govern, but to have some of the "mad people" under them. This seems great responsibility on their part, with less hope of saving the patient.

'He is most ungovernable – in the extremest state of madness; and has been much too ungovernable to take anything but a small quantity of magnesia, for the last twenty-four hours. The physicians are of no use whatever – they have no power or influence – indeed he is incapable of any reasoning whatever.'

November 5, 1810. 'You will see the King announced in the bulletin as better. On Saturday he had not a wink of sleep. On Sunday morning they applied leeches to his temples; he was calmer, and they placed a pillow of hops under his head. He slept on Sunday evening and night six hours; but less to twelve o'clock this day. He has not had the interval of one moment's reason.'

November 7, 1810. 'During the time of the King's most violent raving, his pulse has seldom exceeded eighty. I do not say that during his whole attack it has never been higher; it certainly has, but the malady has been most upon him when the pulse has not been so high. At present he is in a calmer state of mind – that is to say, he is more insensible to what passes – but his reason has not returned, unless it was reason to appear to wish to eat some more potatoes.'

November 11, 1810. 'The account to me of yesterday was, "The King is certainly better. He has slept a good deal, his pulse is at 86, and he knew one of his attendants". The physicians are sanguine of his speedy recovery.'

December 7, 1810. 'You may depend upon it, there is no truth whatever in the report of the fainting fits . . . Willis is very angry with the other physicians, whom he charges with impeding the recovery, by interfering too much, and conversing with him. This shows how little his mind is capable of converse.'

'His position,' commented the Marquis of Buckingham, 'excited the deepest sympathy of an entire and loyal people, except among a small section, who affected republicanism, and the still more selfish group, who, in the eagerness of their worship of the rising sun, forgot their obligations to the light which, for so many years had warmed them with its brilliancy, and had but so recently been eclipsed.'

VIII

Parliament was due to reassemble on 1st November, and it was impossible any longer to keep all knowledge of the state of the King's health from the public. Parliament was therefore adjourned until the 15th, in the hope that the King's health would have improved by that time, and the Prime Minister (Mr Perceval) intimated then that the royal physicians considered that his Majesty's health 'was happily in a state of progressive improvement'.

Enlightened doctors were by this period occasionally successful in dealing with certain forms of insanity. The treatments of the King ranged from the strait waistcoat to 'the warm bath', and none seemed to do more good than the other. His Majesty's intense and avowed hostility to most of his physicians cannot be cited as evidence that they were either incompetent or unkind; and with the Queen's Council and the Houses of Lords and Commons constantly calling them to account they would have been foolish indeed if they had not done their best.

The bulletin, dated 13th November 1810, was signed by H. R. Reynolds, H. Halford, W. Heberden, M. Baillie, and R. Willis. Henry Revell Reynolds, said to have been the last London physician to wear a wig, was Harveian Orator in 1786, the grandfather of Sir John Russell Reynolds (President of the British Medical Association in 1895), and an ancestor of Dr Russell Reynolds, the radiologist of the present generation. Sir Henry Halford, physician to five sovereigns, was one of those adroit physicians whom a Court training forms and of whom there has been a regular succession about the English royal family; he had the complete confidence of the Queen and her family and was employed in many delicate matters. William Heberden the younger was the son of the great physician whose name is perpetuated in 'Heberden's nodes' (a rheumatic condition) – Dr Johnson called him 'the last of the Romans'. Matthew Baillie was the nephew of William and John Hunter and son of the professor of divinity at Glasgow; he was physician to St George's Hospital, president of the College of Physicians, and author of the first textbook of 'Morbid Anatomy' or pathology (1793). Robert Darling Willis was the son of Francis and brother of John Willis and had become a Physician-in-Ordinary to the King.

IX

By the beginning of 1811 the King had almost completely recovered except for two persistent delusions, one that he was Elector of Hanover, the other a resurgence of a romantic passion he had had for the beautiful Countess of Pembroke nearly fifty years previously. The Prime Minister told the King that in the opinion of his physicians he was still scarcely sufficiently recovered to be troubled with public business. 'If I am wanted,' answered the King, 'I shall always be at hand to come forward.' Meanwhile a Regency Bill had been introduced into Parliament, constituting the Prince of Wales Regent of the Realm, under certain restrictive provisions that were to cease at the end of a year. The care of the King's person was to be vested in the Queen. The Royal Princes, with the Regent, protested in writing to the Houses of Parliament against any restrictions on the Regency, and this offended many members of the Commons.

It was universally assumed that the first act of the Regent would be the dismissal of the Tory Ministers and their replacement by his Whig friends; but the disloyal, unprincipled and selfish Prince intimated that he intended to retain the present Ministers in power 'so as not to interfere with the progress of the King's disorder'! Sir Henry Halford and Dr Baillie, the King's physicians, having told the Prince that 'although not probable, it was still quite possible' for the King to recover his faculties. For many months the health of the King fluctuated, his symptoms sometimes raising the hopes of his physicians and at other times causing his family the deepest depression and alarm. By the middle of May it was materially worse, the King continuing to brood over his previous mental derangements. On 20th May he rode in Windsor Great Park, the bells rang and the troops fired a *feu de joie*, but he was never seen outside the walls of Windsor Castle again. In January 1812, the printed evidence of the Royal physicians, as taken before the several Committees of the Houses of Lords and Commons, could have left very little doubt in the minds of the public that the mind of the King was permanently eclipsed.

His sight was increasingly affected by cataract, and the eight remaining years of the existence of King George III were passed, with rare intervals, in both mental and visual darkness, to which was gradually added the further handicap of deafness. The Prince Regent on one occasion heard his afflicted father lamenting his blindness in the words of Milton: 'Oh dark, dark, dark, amid the blaze of noon.' He occupied a suite of apartments on the ground floor of the Castle facing the North Terrace and overlooking the prospect of Eton College and the Thames. Sometimes a startled spectator would glimpse at a window the afflicted King, with long white hair and beard, in a purple dressing-gown with the star of the Garter on his breast. He held animated conversations with the ghosts of departed statesmen, but a remarkable feature of his disorder was that he never forgot that he was King of England. His Queen died at Kew, in November 1818, after a long and painful illness, aged 75; and King George III, having ruled for over sixty years, faded away to nothingness in 1820, mad, blind and deaf, at the age of 81.

X

The five mental illnesses of King George III would be described by a modern psychiatrist as 'periodic psychoses of hypomanic type'. Such a patient is usually extremely elated and very restless, moving about and talking incessantly. His mood changes rapidly to one of anger at the least contradiction or frustration, and the patient then may become impulsive and violent. The patient's physical state reflects his overactivity, his skin flushed and sweating, his pupils dilated, his pulse-rate markedly raised.

For centuries the mentally afflicted were treated as dangerous wild beasts or even put to death as 'possessed by the devil', and their miserable condition in the early part of the eighteenth century is pictured in the well-known engraving after Hogarth. The subject of insanity was, however, frequently brought before the public at this time, and in 1751 St Luke's (mental) Hospital was established by voluntary subscription, situated in Moorfields, opposite the centuries-old St Mary of Bethelem or Bethlem Hospital, founded in 1247, from which is derived the word 'bedlam'.

In 1763 the state of private madhouses in England was examined by a committee of the House of Commons, which included such well-known figures as the elder Pitt and the elder Fox, Wilkes, Lord North, and William Grenville. It came to the conclusion 'that it is the opinion of this committee that the present state of the private mad-houses in this Kingdom requires the interposition of the legislature'. The liberty of the subject could be taken away with alarming facility and frequently individuals availed themselves of a private madhouse to get rid of a troublesome wife or daughter. In 1773 a Bill was passed in the House of Commons for the 'Regulation of Private Mad-houses', but it was thrown out (like other liberal measures) by the House of Lords.

In 1792, William Tuke, a Quaker who was not a physician but a philanthropist, founded The Retreat in York, for the treatment of insane persons without restraint; and in 1798 Philippe Pinel was bold enough to remove the chains that restrained the insane patients of the Bicêtre Hospital in Paris.

There is no doubt that the publicity given to the treatment of the mental illnesses of King George III, with the public examinations of his physicians before committees of both Houses of Parliament, had a beneficent influence upon the more humane treatment of the insane in England.

REFERENCES

Diary and Letters of Madame D'Arblay (1778–1840), edited by Austin Dobson, 6 vols. Macmillan, London 1904–05.

R. BISSET. *History of the Reign of George III*, 6 vols. Longmans, London 1820.

DUKE OF BUCKINGHAM AND CHANDOS. *Memoirs of the Court and Cabinet of George III*, 4 vols. Hurst & Blackett, London 1853–5.

J. HENEAGE JESSE. *Memoirs of the Life and Reign of King George the Third*, 3 vols. Tinsley, London 1867.

w. MUNK. *Roll of Royal College of Physicians*, 2nd ed., London 1878.

D. H. TUKE. *Chapters in the History of the Insane*, Kegan Paul, London 1882.

ANON. (probably Charles Louis Taylor). *Some Royal Death-Beds: George III*. British Medical Journal, June 17th, 1911, p. 1434.

WALTER R. BETT. *George III*. British Medical Journal, Sept. 24th, 1938, Vol. *ii*, p. 664.

DENIS HILL. *Psychiatry*, in SIR JOHN RICHARDSON'S *Practice of Medicine*, Churchill, London 1956.

J. STEVEN WATSON. *The Reign of George III*, 1760–1815, Clarendon Press, Oxford 1960.

c. c. TRENCH. *History Today*, June, 1962, Vol. **xii**, p. 385.

CHAPTER XI

THE DEATH IN CHILDBIRTH OF PRINCESS CHARLOTTE

THE death in childbirth of Princess Charlotte, after she had given birth to a still-born boy, took place on 6th November 1817. She was the only child of the Prince Regent, afterwards King George IV from 1820 to 1830, and the only legitimate grandchild of King George III, although he had seven sons and five daughters, most of whom preferred connubial bliss with a commoner in preference to the terms of the rigidly applied Royal Marriage Act. If Princess Charlotte had lived she would have become Queen of Great Britain and Ireland in 1830, and Queen Victoria would not only not have reigned but in all probability would never even have been born.

In the year 1794 the Prince of Wales, who was to become the Prince Regent in 1811, was in dire financial straits. Parliament had already paid his debts of £180,000 only seven years before, and now he was owing over £600,000 and had had the bailiffs in his house. The times were hardly propitious towards the indulgence of follies and extravagances on this scale, for Britain was at war with revolutionary France since 1793. His father, the King, told him that the only way in which Parliament might be induced to vote enough money to pay his enormous debts was for him to marry a lady of royal birth, in accordance with the Royal Marriage Act, and invite Parliamentary approval of a new and suitable establishment. There were certain difficulties in the way, for the Prince had already in 1785 secretly married a virtuous and well-connected widow aged 27 named Mrs Fitzherbert. This was not only against the Royal Marriage Act, but as she was a Roman Catholic the marriage was illegal according to the Act of Settlement and so could be annulled. Nevertheless, he lived openly with Mrs Fitzherbert, who was treated by Society as his wife, but by 1794 she had been supplanted by a new (but by no means his first) mistress, Lady Jersey. Lady Jersey encouraged the idea of a royal marriage, as it would push Mrs Fitzherbert even farther into the background.

The King chose as his son's prospective bride Princess Caroline of Brunswick, daughter of his sister Princess Augusta and the ruling Duke of Brunswick, nephew of Frederick the Great. In April 1795 the Princess was married by proxy at the Court of Brunswick and brought to England in a man-of-war. She was a gauche and rather simple, voluble young lady, brought up in the dull etiquette of a tiny German Court, and made no appeal to the 'First Gentleman of Europe', accustomed as he was to the intimate company of beautiful, elegant and sophisticated women. When he met her for the first time he embraced her and then walked to the end of the room and demanded a glass of brandy. Three days later the Prince and the Princess were married at the Chapel Royal, St James's, and Parliament settled his debts and increased his allowances. Within a few weeks the Prince was beginning to live apart from his wife – when she was in London he was in Brighton and *vice versa* – but the public received with joy the news that the Princess was pregnant.

On 7th January 1796, a princess was born at Carlton House and christened Charlotte Augusta. She did not have so much an unhappy childhood as an unfortunate upbringing. The Prince showed little interest in her except as a weapon against his estranged wife, from whom he tried unsuccessfully to rid himself by a 'Delicate Investigation' of her mildly indiscreet conduct – it was solemnly stated, for instance, that 'she had played blind-man's buff with two gentlemen present', and most of the witnesses were discontented maidservants and footmen. Later on, however, when they were finally separated and Queen Caroline went to live abroad, her indiscretions became more notorious and even eccentric, though an attempted divorce was abortive.

The Prince became Prince Regent because of the mental incapacity of his father and forthwith deserted the Whigs for the Tories, the King's party, so that Henry Brougham and the Whigs in opposition began to take an interest in the welfare of Princess Charlotte. She was allowed to have an establishment and was brought up by a succession of governesses and sub-governesses. Her natural vanity was encouraged by her entourage, who constantly pandered to her splendid destiny as heir-presumptive to the throne of England. At the age of 17 she is described as being 'well-built, not beautiful but agreeable with regular features, light hair and pale blue eyes'. She was self-willed and coltish, but cheerful and kindly, intelligent and with a friendly manner. Her marriage began to be discussed, and the candidate for her hand who was supported by her father was William, Hereditary Prince of Orange, who afterwards became King of the Netherlands. Although a marriage contract had been signed, the engagement collapsed on the point of the Princess having to leave England for at least part of the year and live in Holland after the marriage, an idea which was vigorously opposed by the Whigs and indeed by herself and by the general public.

In June, 1814, Princess Charlotte, who meanwhile had had other mild flirtations, at the peace celebrations in London noticed the handsome appearance of young Prince Leopold of Saxe-Coburg, who was one of the officers in attendance on the Emperor Alexander of Russia. Prince Leopold was a younger son without any fortune except his good looks, who had joined the Russian army and fought in the Napoleonic wars. He was ambitious, and unlike the Prince of Orange, there was no reason why he should not live in England, so in 1816 Princess Charlotte consented to marry him. He became naturalized as a British subject, an annual allowance of £60,000 was voted by Parliament, and a furnished residence in London, Camelford House in Park Lane, was taken for the bride and bridegroom. The Prince made it his business to study the language, history, laws and customs of England, and brought with him from

Germany his trusted physician and private secretary Dr Stockmar. The wedding took place on 2nd May 1816, in the Grand Saloon of Carlton House, where an altar had been set up, and the honeymoon was spent at Oatlands Park, near Weybridge, seat of the Duke of York. In addition to Camelford House, the young couple had Clare-mont, in Surrey, 14 miles from London, as their country home, and there they spent most of their time. 'This marriage,' wrote Princess Charlotte, 'makes my whole happiness.' She had one and perhaps two early miscarriages, but a child was expected towards the end of 1817. She was prepared for her confinement, according to the medical custom of the day, by being bled and purged at intervals, for the Princess was considered to be 'of a plethoric habit', which had to be 'lowered'.

II

The newspapers announced that the confinement was to be ex-pected in October, and the Princess preferred to stay at Claremont for it. Sir Richard Croft, Bart. (he had recently succeeded to the family baronetcy through the death of his elder brother), aged 55, the leading English man-midwife or obstetrician of the day, was in attendance, and he and Dr Matthew Baillie, physician to the Princess (and nephew of William and John Hunter), came to stay at Clare-mont. As often happens with a first child, the confinement was delayed longer than anticipated, and the two physicians remained at Claremont for over three weeks. Croft and Baillie were brothers-in-law, having married the twin daughters of Dr Thomas Denman, whose teachings and textbook dominated the midwifery of the late eighteenth and early nineteenth centuries.

Labour pains began on the evening of Monday, 3rd November, and at 3 a.m. on the Tuesday, Croft sent express messages to the Ministers of State, whose duty it was to be present at the birth of an heir presumptive to the throne. The Archbishop of Canterbury, the Bishop of London, the Lord Chancellor, the Home Secretary, the Chancellor of the Exchequer, and the Secretary for War all arrived in their coaches-and-four before 8 a.m. They were to have a long vigil.

For 26 hours labour pains continued, but they were weak though sharp and distressing, and labour progressed very slowly, though 26 hours is not unduly prolonged for the first stage of labour in the confinement of a woman with her first child. But the pains continued to be feeble and Croft wisely would not consider the use of forceps without a consultation with another accoucheur. Accordingly before midnight on the Tuesday (4th November) he dispatched a note to Dr John Sims, as had been arranged if it were considered necessary. Dr Sims, aged 69, held an appointment as physician to Princess Charlotte and also honorary appointments as accoucheur and as physician to various charitable institutions in London – though he is described as 'botanist and physician' (in that order) in the *Dictionary of National Biography*. The well-known Sims speculum, still in use, was designed not by him but by Dr James Marion Sims of South Carolina, U.S.A., later in the nineteenth century.

Dr Sims arrived at 2 a.m. on 5th November, when the second stage of labour had been going on for five hours, but he did not see the Princess and remained in an adjoining room. Instruments were ready and at hand, 'but the employment of them never became a question'.

Obstetric forceps were invented by Peter Chamberlen the elder, a Hugenot refugee, about the year 1600, and the invention was kept a secret in four generations of the Chamberlen family for 125 years. Dr Hugh Chamberlen died in 1728, leaving no son to carry on the secret, which then became gradually known among surgeons. In 1818 several pairs of forceps were found in the attic of a manor-house in Essex, which had formerly belonged to the Chamberlen family. William Giffard in 1726 was the first to use obstetric forceps after the Chamberlens, and Edmund Chapman in 1733 was the first to describe and illustrate them. Dr Douglas Guthrie, otologist and medical historian, quotes Professor Miles Phillips, the Sheffield obstetrician, as follows: 'Chapman did not invent the "English lock", as still used, though some authors think so: he certainly did away with the screw (a French idea) and used a simple groove on each blade. It was the famous William Smellie (of Glasgow and later of London) who, in 1744–5, added flanges to the grooves and so contrived the "English lock", and he is usually credited with this invention.' At first Smellie employed wooden forceps in order to avoid the clinking noise of the metal blades – for forceps were unpopular with both patients and midwives – and later on had the blades covered with leather. He also modified the shape of the forceps and added the pelvic curves.

At 9 p.m. when the second stage of labour had lasted for 24 hours, the child, a boy weighing nine pounds, was born dead, and had evidently been dead for some hours. When the Princess was told this she took it calmly, and was in fact relieved that the prolonged labour was over. During the labour she had been quite strong and able to be out of bed from time to time, walking about the rooms. A bulletin stated that Princess Charlotte 'had been delivered of a stillborn male child and was doing extremely well'.

About ten minutes after the birth of the child Croft found that the womb was still acting irregularly and told Sims that he suspected 'hour-glass contraction' with the placenta (afterbirth) in the upper part. They agreed that nothing should be done unless haemorrhage came on; after 20 minutes haemorrhage did come on and Croft carried out manual removal of the placenta. When it was separated a strong pain occurred and the womb (as was hoped) contracted. For the next two hours Croft felt no apprehension, and the physicians retired to their bedrooms, leaving their patient in the care of Mrs Griffiths, the nurse, for they considered that for the remainder of the night she should be kept as quiet as possible. She took some gruel, but found difficulty in swallowing it. She then complained of severe chilliness and a pain at her stomach, and Mrs Griffiths instantly called up the physicians. They found her pulse rapid, feeble

M

and irregular, and she was extremely restless. Cordials, anti-spasmodic and opiate medicines were given.

Baron Stockmar (as the doctor afterwards became) gives a vivid account in his *Memoirs*. 'Dr Baillie sent to say that he wished I would see the Princess. I hesitated, but at last I went with him. She was in a state of great suffering and disquiet from spasms in the chest and difficulty in breathing, tossed about incessantly from one side to the other, speaking now to Baillie, now to Croft. Baillie said to her "Here comes an old friend of yours". She stretched out her left hand eagerly to me and pressed mine twice vehemently. I felt her pulse, which was very quick; the beats now full, now weak, now inter-mittent. Baillie kept giving her wine constantly. She said to me, "They have made me tipsy!" For about a quarter of an hour I went in and out of the room, then the rattle in the throat began. I had just left the room when she called out loudly "Stocky! Stocky!" I went back; she was quieter, but the rattle continued. She turned more than once over on her face, drew her legs up, and her hands grew cold. At two o'clock in the morning of 6th November 1817 — therefore about five hours after the birth of the child — she was no more.'

Strange rumours of foul play got abroad; it was pointed out that not one of the numerous royal matrons were with the Princess; the public were almost hysterical; and the physicians were accused of ignorance, mismanagement and neglect. Poor Croft was accused of 'lowering' Princess Charlotte too greatly during her pregnancy by excessive bleeding and a low diet; of not allowing Sims to come into the room until the final moments; of going to bed and leaving his patient in charge of the nurse. The medical attack was led by Jesse Foot, a well-known surgeon who was, however, notoriously vindictive and jealous: he was the author of a *Life of John Hunter*, in which he did all he could to defame that great man. He wrote letters to newspapers and published pamphlets 'On the necessity of a Public Inquiry into the cause of death of the Princess Charlotte'. Henry Brougham wrote: 'Her death produced throughout the

Kingdom the feelings of the deepest sorrow and most bitter disappointment. It is scarcely possible to exaggerate, and it is difficult for persons not living at the time to believe, how universal and how genuine those feelings were. It really was as if every household throughout Great Britain had lost a favourite child.'

Lord Byron inserted six verses on the tragedy in the fourth canto of *Childe Harold's Pilgrimage*, of which verse *CLXX* should be quoted:

> *Of sackcloth was thy wedding garment made;*
> *The bridal's fruit is ashes: in the dust*
> *The fair-hair'd Daughter of the Isles is laid,*
> *The love of millions! How we did entrust*
> *Futurity to her! and, though it must*
> *Darken above our bones, yet fondly deem'd*
> *Our children should obey her child, and bless'd*
> *Her and her hoped-for seed, whose promise seem'd*
> *Like stars to shepherds' eyes: — 'twas but a meteor beam'd.*

It was then the custom for the Serjeant Surgeon to embalm members of the Royal Family, and as during this process every organ was removed and treated separately, it amounted to a very complete post-mortem examination. This was carried out by Sir Everard Home on 7th November – he was connected with Dr Baillie, as he was a brother-in-law of William and John Hunter. He reported that the hour-glass contraction of the womb was still very apparent and that it contained a considerable quantity of blood. The pericardium (the covering of the heart) contained two ounces of red-coloured fluid. The child was well-formed, and every part of its internal structure was quite sound.

III

What then was the explanation of the tragedy? Sir Eardley Holland, the eminent obstetrician, has written: 'Anyone who has tried to discover anything new about Charlotte's confinement has had to give up in despair. The authentic sources of information are scanty and already well explored, whilst the larger amount of material has, heretofore, been found in sources which, to a medical historian, are suspect but which, nevertheless, have proved most tempting to Charlotte's many biographers.' In the year 1949, however, Sir Eardley Holland had the good fortune to be introduced to (the late) Lord Croft, great-great-grandson of Sir Richard Croft, who was much interested in his ancestor and had just found some important letters. A little later he also met Major Richard Croft, another great-great-grandson, who had discovered some even more important documents, and into whose possession all the letters and documents have now passed. There is also, in the library of the Royal College of Surgeons, among the Hunter-Baillie papers there, an account in the handwriting of Mrs Baillie, 'Dr Baillie's account of Princess Charlotte's labour'. Dr Baillie wrote to Croft: 'I thought it proper to leave a copy of the general statement with the Queen and I enclose another which you should carry to Carlton House to the Prince Regent.'

Croft himself comments as follows (in the unpublished family papers):

'The cause of H.R.H.'s death, as it was quite unexpected until half past twelve, so it is still somewhat obscure. The symptoms were such as precede death from haemorrhage; but the quantity of blood lost was scarcely sufficient to create any alarm, being less than usual on such occasions, yet, added to about a pound of blood found in the cavity of the uterus (womb), might have been enough to produce the unfavourable symptoms in so excitable a constitution. It is most possible that the two ounces of fluid found in the pericardium were poured out during the violence of the spasmodic affection of the chest, and if so it must have had very great influence in preventing the heart from recovering its regular and vigorous action, and it is possible it might have been deposited earlier and thus have produced all the distressing symptoms, and have had more to do with the fatal issue than has been imagined.'

'It seems hardly possible to doubt,' says Sir Eardley Holland in his Fletcher Shaw Memorial Lecture (1951), 'that Charlotte died of postpartum haemorrhage. Four haemorrhages are recorded, the first before the placenta was removed, the second during its removal, the third when it was taken from the vagina, and the fourth, the concealed haemorrhage in the uterus found after death. None was severe, but their cumulative effect must have been considerable. Charlotte's symptoms, from near midnight until her death 2½ hours later, were typical of blood loss, slowly mounting, the lethal phase being a slow leak into the uterus.'

The management of Princess Charlotte's labour must be judged in the light of the midwifery practice of that day. Even today, 20 per cent of the deaths in childbirth are from postpartum haemorrhage and shock. The chief criticism is that Croft allowed labour to go on so long without using the forceps. But, as Sir Eardley Holland points out, by the principles and rules of contemporary practice, he was not wrong. Dr Thomas Denman wrote in 1801: 'It has long been established as a general rule in this country, that the use of instruments of any kind ought not to be allowed in the practice of midwifery from any motives of eligibility' (i.e. of choice, election or expediency). One has to admit that Croft acted strictly according to Denman, for he was not the sort of man to deviate from his rules of practice by doing something unconventional and perhaps risky. He was trained by Denman, became his assistant, married his daughter, and inherited his practice. 'It is impossible,' wrote the shrewd Baron Stockmar, 'to resist the conviction that the Princess was sacrificed to professional theories.'

Today, ideas have changed. Even in 1879 Robert Barnes, the Victorian obstetrician, wrote that 'we should wait to see what the woman is able to accomplish, not what she can endure'. And De Lee, professor of obstetrics at Chicago, has written: 'In general it is wise to operate (i.e. use forceps) long before the exhaustion is marked, before the signs and symptoms of threatened rupture of the uterus are present, and before the child presents evidence of asphyxia. It is impossible to assign an arbitrary limit. As a general rule one should not wait more than one or one and one-half hours after the head has reached the perineum and progress has ceased.'

IV

With the death of Princess Charlotte the Hanoverian succession was in danger, and the Royal Dukes hastened to discard their long-established mistresses and marry German princesses in accordance with the Royal Marriage Act. The Duke of Cambridge had a son in 1819; but two months later, on 24th May, his elder brother, the Duke of Kent (having abandoned Madame St Laurent after 27 years of happy domesticity), had a daughter named Victoria, by the sister of the unfortunate Prince Leopold of Saxe-Coburg.

Prince Leopold decided to settle in England and lived on at Claremont with an allowance from Parliament of £50,000 a year; but after the birth of his niece Victoria he (accompanied by Baron Stockmar) was fortunate enough to be invited to become King of the new kingdom of the Belgians, and married a daughter of King Louis-Philippe of France. At the insistence of his adviser, wise Baron Stockmar, he reluctantly surrendered his £50,000 annual Parliamentary grant.

Sir Richard Croft, although the Royal Family were most considerate and sympathetic towards him, was overwhelmed with criticism, and some of his distinguished patients wrote to him declining his further services. Despite his skill and experience, he was a diffident and sensitive man. Three months after the death of the Princess Charlotte he was in attendance on a lady in childbirth with complications resembling those of the Princess. She was a Mrs Thackeray, wife of the Provost of King's College, Cambridge (a second cousin of W. M. Thackeray), who was being confined in London at the house of her sister, Miss Cottin, 86 Wimpole Street. A baby girl was born safely (who grew up to be a wealthy spinster, Mary Ann Thackeray, and lived until 1879), but the mother died in childbirth. Sir Richard Croft, in despair, shot himself with a pistol which he found in the room that he was occupying in the house.

REFERENCES

THOMAS DENMAN. *An Introduction to the Practice of Midwifery*, 2 vols. J. Johnson, London 1801.

JESSE FOOT. *A letter on the necessity of a public enquiry into the cause and death of the Pss. Charlotte* (pamphlet). 18th Nov. 1817.

BARON STOCKMAR. *Memoirs*, by his son E. von Stockmar, edited by F. Max Müller. 2 vols. Longmans, London 1872.

LADY R. WEIGALL. *A Brief Memoir of the Princess Charlotte*, John Murray, London 1874.

PERCY FITZGERALD. *Life of George the Fourth*, 2 vols. Tinsley, London 1881.

G. J. RENIER. *The Ill-fated Princess*, Peter Davies, London 1932.

J. B. DE LEE. *Principles and Practice of Obstetrics*, 7th edition. Saunders, Philadelphia and London 1938 (first published in 1913).

COLIN MACDONALD. *The Case of the Princess Charlotte*. Medical Journal of Australia, 11th Jan. 1941, p. 38.

DOUGLAS GUTHRIE. *A History of Medicine*, Nelson, London 1945.

SIR EARDLEY HOLLAND. *The Princess Charlotte of Wales: a triple obstetric tragedy.* Journal of Obstetrics and Gynaecology of the British Empire, Dec. 1951, Vol. **58**, p. 905.

D. M. STUART. *Daughter of England*, Macmillan, London 1952. (With a Medical Appendix on the cause of Princess Charlotte's Death.)

BRUCE DICKINS. Times Lit. Supp., 13th Oct. 1961, p. 690.

CHAPTER XII

THE FATAL LARYNGITIS OF GEORGE WASHINGTON

WHEN George Washington died, on 14th December 1799, the manner of his death quickly became the subject of controversy, which has never been satisfactorily settled. The announcement of his death came as a great shock to the country, for the public had been accustomed to look upon him as a man of tremendous physical vigour, and, even at the age of 68, it was unbelievable that he should have died from a cold and sore throat of only forty-eight hours duration.

II

George Washington's father had extensive estates in Virginia, and each of his several sons inherited a separate plantation. George, the eldest son by his second wife, was born on 22nd February 1732, but left the local school at 15, without even having begun the study of the classics, though he had a good working knowledge of the English language. He devoted his last two years at school to the study of geometry, trigonometry, and surveying, and took up the profession of a surveyor, which was then and there a lucrative one. The systematic habits, clear diagrams, precise tables, and neat handwriting which he acquired then were of great value to him in later life. Soon after leaving school he went to live with his elder half-brother Lawrence at his home on the Potomac River, Mount Vernon, and there he made friends with the Fairfax family, one of whom was married to his brother. The eccentric bachelor Lord Fairfax, who had inherited some millions of acres of land in Virginia, came over from England to examine it, and liked the country so much that he built a mansion and settled in the Shenandoah Valley, where he lived to the age of 92.

Lawrence Washington developed pulmonary tuberculosis and was advised to go to the balmier climate of Barbados, whither his brother George accompanied him. After only a short time at Barbados George contracted smallpox, but was fortunate in making a good recovery in three weeks, though his face showed permanent marks of the disease. Altogether he was away for four months – the only time he was ever abroad from America – but his half-brother's health did not improve and Lawrence came home to Virginia, where he died at the age of 34, leaving large estates, to which George became the residuary legatee.

George Washington was six feet three inches in height, with a strong, erect frame, large hands and long legs, strongly marked features, with prominent nose and chin. His manner was dignified and rather solemn, he had blue eyes, wore his brown hair powdered, and had to have most of his teeth pulled; his thin lips in the well-known portrait by Gilbert Stuart owe their unattractive appearance to the ill-fitting primitive dentures that he was wearing. He enjoyed dancing, attended the theatre at Williamsburg or Annapolis, but his chief recreation was fox-hunting, going out two or three times a week, and shooting, especially wild duck.

In January 1759 George Washington married an attractive widow with two children, Mrs Martha Custis, who was 'distinguished for her beauty, accomplishments, and wealth', and to whom he continued happily married for forty years. With his wife's added to his own estates Washington became one of the wealthiest, besides being one of the most enterprising, of Virginia tobacco-planters. He conducted his plantations with the help mainly of negro slaves, and exported his tobacco to London, Bristol and Liverpool.

At the age of 19 Washington had become an officer in the local militia, and was actively engaged in preventing Indian depredations and French encroachments on the western frontier of Virginia. In the spring of 1755 he joined General Braddock, who had arrived from England with two regiments of regular troops; they fought a disastrous battle with the French and Indians at Monongahela, for the British soldiers obstinately formed into platoons and columns against an invisible guerrilla enemy, concealed in deep ravines and firing from behind trees and bushes, and more than half of the British troops were killed or wounded. Washington had four bullets through his coat and two horses were shot under him, but escaped unhurt; General Braddock himself received a mortal wound.

Colonel Washington was then appointed Commander-in-chief of the Virginia forces, and spent the next two years defending the border outposts against Indian raiders. But the fever (probably malaria, for the swamps were full of mosquitoes), which had already attacked him before Monongahela, returned in 1757, when he was also seriously ill with a 'bloody flux', and his physician insisted that he must retire from the army, at the early age of 26. He was elected from Frederick County to the House of Burgesses of Virginia, which met at Williamsburg, continuing so for fifteen years, and three months after his marriage he established himself and his family at Mount Vernon.

III

The crisis was now approaching which was to engage George Washington in a wider sphere of action. The complaints and remonstrances of the American colonists had made no other impression on the British Ministry than to confirm them in their acts of repression and severity. After the Boston 'tea-party' in 1773 an Act of Parliament was passed shutting up the port of Boston and inflicting other disabilities on the inhabitants of that town, many of whom were in fact loyal to the British Government. Letters were received at Williamsburg from Boston, calling on the people of the American colonies generally to enter into an agreement not to hold any further commercial intercourse with Great Britain, either by imports or exports. A general Congress of representatives of the various colonies was held at Philadelphia on 5th September 1774, which drafted a petition to King George III and an address to the people of Great Britain, the latter affirming that 'You have been told, that we are seditious, impatient of government, and desirous of independency. Be assured, that these are not facts, but calumnies.'

As early as 1759 Lord Camden had said in London to Benjamin Franklin: 'In spite of all your talk about your loyalty, you Americans, in spite of your boasted affection for England, I know that some day you will cast off the ties which bind you to her, and will raise the flag of independence.' 'No such idea,' replied Franklin, 'exists, or will get into the heads of the Americans, unless you maltreat them very scandalously.'

And in 1774, when independence was becoming inevitable, George Washington wrote to his friend Captain Mackenzie of the British Army, then stationed at Boston: 'You are taught to believe that the people of Massachusetts are a lot of rebels, in arms for independence, and what not. Let me tell you, my dear friend, you are deceived, greatly deceived. I can bear witness, as a fact, that independence is neither the wish nor the interest of that colony, nor of any other on the continent, separately or collectively; but, at the same time, you may make certain that none of them will ever submit to the loss of those privileges, of those precious rights, which are essential to the happiness of every free state, and without which liberty, property, life, are deprived of every security.'

In 1774, coming out of the first Congress formed to prepare for the revolution, Patrick Henry, one of the leading republicans, was asked by a friend who was the first man in the Congress. 'If you speak of eloquence,' he answered, 'Mr Rutledge of South Carolina is by far the greatest orator. But if you speak of a solid knowledge of things and sound judgement, Colonel Washington is unquestionably the greatest man in the assembly.'

Washington had not those brilliant and extraordinary qualities which appeal at first glance to the human imagination. But when the necessity arrived, without effort on his own part and without surprise in others, the sagacious Virginian planter proved himself a great man. He was not afraid to take responsibility, he acted resolutely, and he had implicit faith in his own judgement. Washington was convinced that the cause of his country was just, and to a cause so just success would not be wanting. To achieve independence by war, nine years were necessary, but not for a moment was his faith or his hope shaken. When he was appointed Commander-in-chief of the Continental Army and proceeded to its headquarters at Cambridge, Massachusetts, he found an irregular conglomeration of some 17,000 militia from the various colonies, without general organization, many of them sick, united only by mutual consent, with no supply of clothing, no cash, but few tents and stores, and very little ammunition; discipline was slack and disorders frequent. It was the business of Washington to create a regular army and a military system, and this in time he achieved.

The merit of Washington as a general has been disputed, and it is true that he did not give those glittering manifestations of military genius that in Europe have made the renown of great generals. But, operating as he did with a little army in wide open spaces, strategy on the grand scale and great battles were out of his range. But more than once, when the opportunity arose, the boldness of the general was shown as well as the bravery of the man. In 1776, in the midst of a retreat and during a rigorous frost, with troops in poor shape and half-disbanded, Washington suddenly resumed the offensive, attacked successively at Trenton and Princeton different corps of the British army, and won two battles in eight days. In the winter of 1777–8 he established a fortified encampment at Valley Forge, twenty miles from Philadelphia, cutting down the trees to build huts, and there the army remained until the following June, ill-housed and ill-fed, on the point of exhaustion. But Washington kept it together, through intrigues, disloyalties, and constant criticism from a hostile Congress.

To Washington must be given the credit of the final victorious blow of the war, the capture of Cornwallis and his army at York-town, and he was present when the American army entered New York in triumph in November, 1783. Then he went south to Anna-polis and resigned his commission as Commander-in-chief to the Congress in session there, leaving his expenses (for he had refused a salary) to be discharged by the Treasury.

For the next four years George Washington was occupied on his estates; he enlarged the Mount Vernon house in 1786, and he laid out his grounds in a new design. He enjoyed being a generous host, and 'he and his household seldom sat down to dinner alone'.

But when the time came to elect the first President, all eyes turned to Washington, and the electors cast a unanimous vote for him. He was inaugurated in New York, and during the next eight years his administration was marked by the caution and wisdom that already were his chief characteristics. His first cabinet, evenly balanced between the two parties, was outstanding, formed by Thomas Jefferson as Secretary of State, Alexander Hamilton as Secretary of the Treasury, Henry Knox as Secretary for War, and Edmund Randolph as Attorney-General. But the members of his cabinet were mere heads of departments, as indeed they are today in America, and there was no collective responsibility, as in Britain. Washington, as has been said, knew something nobler and more difficult than to make war; he knew how to govern.

IV

As President, Washington was more powerful than the King in England, whose state some of his critics considered that he aped. He drove in a coach-and-four – at the opening of Congress in a coach-and-six, with outriders in livery, at state functions wore black velvet court dress with gold buckles and a dress sword, had a weekly levée open to all, accepted no outside hospitality, and his wife was called 'Lady Washington'. To his authority, however, must be attributed the sucess of the constitution, for at the first session of the new Congress the representatives were so casual that a quorum could not be formed on the appointed day. By the end of Washington's first term of office the constitution had been firmly established, the members of Congress were representative of the best elements in the nation, and it was held in high popular esteem.

He was reluctant to be re-elected to a second term of office, but his reluctance was overcome by popular acclaim, and his election was again unanimous. Difficulties soon arose through the changed relations with France. The French Revolution had at first been hailed by all Americans as the dawn of liberty in Europe, but as it developed into anarchy, frenzy and massacre the educated classes were revolted and began to sympathize more with the ordered liberty of England, though the masses still supported the French Jacobins, whatever their crimes.

When France declared war on Britain in 1793, Genet, a young French envoy to America, used its ports to fit out privateers against the British commercial ships, and was wildly applauded by cheering crowds when prizes were brought into Philadelphia, then the political capital. Washington, however, proclaimed neutrality and enforced it, as only he could have done, against the popular will and against the inclination of Jefferson, his Secretary of State, who, a sincere and dedicated democrat, openly sympathized with the French revolution.

Under the guidance of Washington, and with the benefit of the conservative financial and federalist policy of Hamilton, the young American republic weathered its early storms, and found itself respected among the community of nations. Washington began to feel himself growing old and deaf (the latter perhaps as a result of the crude quinine, or chinchona bark, with which his fevers had been treated), and resolutely refused to accept nomination for a third term of office. Probably he belonged to an age that was already passing. In March 1797, he retired to his pleasant home at Mount Vernon, and devoted the remaining years of his life to his family and his estates. In the famous words of Henry Lee, 'he was first in war, first in peace, and first in the hearts of his countrymen'.

V

Washington's health had on the whole been good, but with spells of sometimes severe illness. The earliest illness of which there is any record is the smallpox which he contracted at the age of 19 in Barbados, though shortly after his return home he had what he called 'a violent attack of pleurisy which reduced me very low'. During the campaign with General Braddock, when aged 23, he was, as has been noted, stricken with a 'fever', and was 'relieved by the General's ordering a physician to give me Dr James's powder, one of the most excellent medicines in the world. It gave me immediate relief and removed my fever and complaints in four days'. Dr James's powder was a mixture of antimonious oxide and calcium phosphates; it acted as a diaphoretic.

Two years later Washington was apparently attacked by dysentery, with a fever, which returned from time to time, 'in spite of all efforts of the sons of Aesculapius'. 'At certain periods,' he wrote, 'I have been reduced to great extremity and have much reason to apprehend an approaching decay being visited with several symptoms of such a disease.'

Washington was always very pessimistic when he was ill, and on several occasions wrote about his impending dissolution. In 1761 the illness from which he suffered was probably malaria, and he had considerable pain and disturbed sleep. He wrote: 'I was very near my last gasp. The indisposition increased upon me and I fell into a very low and dangerous state. I once thought the grim King would overcome my best efforts and that I must sink in spite of a noble strength.'

In March 1768, his diary contains a pessimistic account of an attack of dysentery, and on two nights the doctor stayed with him. But in a week he was out fox-hunting again. In September, 1786, he had attacks of 'ague'; their periodicity denotes that the illness was in fact malaria, and he had relief from the 'bark' prescribed by his friend Dr Craik. Soon after assuming the office of President,

Washington had a severe attack of what was called anthrax, but which was more probably a carbuncle, situated on the left hip. This caused great pain and discomfort, and he was confined to his house for six weeks. He was attended by Dr Samuel Bard, an Edinburgh graduate and the leading physician of New York, who opened the abscess, and when he went out he had a special couch constructed in his coach, so that he could lie at full length.

In 1790 the seat of government was moved from New York to Philadelphia, and in the spring of that year Washington contracted what appears to have been pneumonia. 'I have already within less than a year,' he wrote, 'had two severe attacks, the last worse than the first. A third more than probably, will put me to sleep with my fathers. At what distance this will be, I know not. I am thankful that I am so well recovered, though I still feel the remains of the violent affection of the lungs, the cough, the pain in my breast, shortness of breath, not having entirely left me.'

In a letter which Jefferson wrote to James Madison on 9th June 1793, he said: 'The President is not well; little lingering fevers have been hanging about him for a week or ten days and affecting his look most remarkably.' Certainly in the last year of his life his health began to fail. On 20th August 1799, he wrote to a correspondent: 'No account of weather etc. kept from hence to the end, on account of a sickness commenced with a fever on the 19th and lasted until the 24th, which left me debilitated.' And later in the same year he wrote, explaining his previous failure to write, 'on account of debilitated health occasioned by the fever, which deprived me of 20 lbs. of weight I had when you and I were at Troy Mill Scales, rendering writing irksome'.

On the morning of 12th December 1799, George Washington spent several hours in the saddle, riding round his plantation and giving directions to his managers. He returned late in the afternoon, wet and chilled with rain and snow, to which he had been exposed when riding home. When he came in his secretary, Tobias Lear, brought him some letters and commented that his neck was wet and some flakes of snow still clung to his hair; but Washington said that his greatcoat had kept him dry, and he went directly in to dinner, which had been kept waiting for him. Next day a heavy fall of snow prevented his going out, but in the early afternoon the snow ceased, and by 4 o'clock it was perfectly clear, so he went as far as his front lawn and marked certain trees to be cut down. He passed the evening with his wife and his secretary, read the newspapers and conversed cheerfully with them until his usual hour for going to bed. Lear suggested that the General should take something for his cold, but he made light of it and said that he preferred to let a cold 'go as it came'.

During the night he had a rigor, a 'severe ague', and before dawn next morning he woke his wife and told her that he felt ill; he breathed with difficulty and could scarcely speak, but would not allow his wife to call anyone. When the housemaid came to make the morning fire at 7 a.m. Mrs Washington sent her to call Tobias Lear and also to send for Rawlins, one of the overseers, to come and bleed him, as it would be some time before the doctor could arrive.

Lear dispatched his own servant for Washington's friend, Dr James Craik, a Scotsman who had studied medicine at Edinburgh and lived nine miles off, at Alexandria. As no relief was obtained from bleeding, a soft cloth soaked in sal volatile was wrapped round his throat and his feet were bathed in hot water. The symptoms were now such as to alarm the family, so another messenger was dispatched for Dr Gustavus Richard Brown, another Edinburgh graduate, who lived near Mount Vernon, at Port Tobacco. At that period Edinburgh had become the most famous medical school in the world, and many American doctors were educated there; between 1749, when the first one graduated, and the end of the century, 117 Americans became M.D.s of Edinburgh.

Dr Craik made the diagnosis of 'inflammatory quinsy', put a blister of cantharides on the throat in the hope of 'drawing the inflammation to the surface', and did a second bleeding. Washington was able to inhale from a steam kettle of vinegar and water, but was

N

unable to gargle, which sounds as if the pharynx, not the larynx, was affected. Dr Craik was anxious for another opinion, and as Dr Brown had not yet come, another messenger was sent to Dr Elisha Cullen Dick of Alexandria, who arrived about 3 p.m. He was an intelligent young physician of 37, a graduate of the University of Pennsylvania, who had been apprenticed to the famous Dr Benjamin Rush (one of the 'Signers' of the Declaration of Independence), and to the distinguished Dr William Shippen, both graduates of Edinburgh, as were all six of the first professors who founded the medical school of Pennsylvania in 1765, the first in America. He suggested that the trachea should be opened in order to give the patient air and as the only hope he saw for him. Tracheotomy was occasionally performed in the seventeenth and eighteenth centuries, as a last resort, but not commonly until mid-nineteenth century. He also deprecated further bleeding, but was overruled. Dr Brown now arrived, and after a consultation with the two others, observing that Washington could now swallow a little, a dose of calomel and tartar emetic was prescribed.

There is no mention anywhere that the interior of the throat was examined, and Dr W. A. Wells, a laryngologist as well as a medical historian, states that he believes that this was never done. The pharynx only might have been examined, for the laryngoscope was not invented for another fifty-six years.

Washington's suffering was acute and unabated through the day, but he bore it with composure and resignation. He asked his wife to bring him the two wills from his desk and directed her to burn one of them; the other was placed in her closet. He also asked his secretary to arrange his accounts and settle his books; in the late afternoon he was helped to a chair, but in half an hour asked to be put back to bed. 'I die hard,' he said, 'but I am not afraid to die.' He addressed his three doctors: 'I feel myself going. I thank you for your attention. You had better not take any more trouble about me, but let me go off quietly. I cannot last long.'

Soft poultices of wheat bran were applied to his throat and

blisters to his legs and feet, and it was said that his breathing seemed less difficult. A little after 10 p.m. on 14th December 1799, his breathing became much easier and Washington lay quietly, his mind perfectly clear. There was a change in his countenance; Lear, his secretary, called Dr Craik to the bedside, and Washington lapsed into unconsciousness.

VI

Dissensions sprang up almost immediately. Washington's doctors were blamed, particularly for excessive bleeding; but bleeding was the orthodox treatment of the times, and possibly even did some good. His disease has been called variously acute laryngitis, diphtheria, acute oedema of the larynx, and quinsy; the diagnosis of his doctors, as given in a statement five days after his death, was 'cynanche trachealis'.

The name 'cynanche' was given at that time to all inflammations of the throat and neck, as indeed was 'quinsy', which was not, as now, restricted to peritonsillar abscess. Dr John Fothergill, the Quaker physician of London, who was a friend of the American colonists and especially of Benjamin Franklin, published in 1748 his classical *Account of the Sore Throat attended with Ulcers*. It has been called the first description of diphtheria, but a careful reading shows it to be rather a description of a malignant type of scarlet fever with tonsillitis.

The history of the case of George Washington does not resemble diphtheria, as it has sometimes been called, unlikely in any case in a man of his years. Dr W. A. Wells has made out a case for its being an acute inflammatory oedema of the larynx, due possibly to a streptococcal infection; but that does not sound very likely in the late stages, as there was no struggling for breath, and death certainly did not result from asphyxia. My own opinion is – mainly because of the short duration of the inflammation, the difficulty in gargling, and the signs and symptoms described briefly but accurately – that in its early stage the condition was probably a true quinsy, a peritonsillar abscess, which was not opened and so tracked down towards the larynx, as happened within my knowledge to a well-known English actor in the prime of life. Death was probably due to broncho-pneumonia, following the throat infection.

REFERENCES

JOHN FOTHERGILL. *Account of the Sore Throat attended with Ulcers,* C. Davis, London 1748.

JOHN MARSHALL. *Life of George Washington,* 5 vols. Wayne, Philadelphia 1807.

JARED SPARKS. *Life of George Washington,* 2 vols. Colburn, London 1839.

M. GUIZOT. *Monk and Washington: historical studies,* Routledge, London 1851.

F. S. OLIVER. *Alexander Hamilton: an essay on American union,* Constable, London 1906.

GOLDWIN SMITH. *The United States: an outline of political history,* Macmillan, New York 1907.

WALTER A. WELLS. *Last Illness and Death of Washington.* Virginia Medical Monthly, 1927, Vol. 53, p. 629.

J. A. CARROLL and MARY W. ASHWORTH (completing the biography of Douglas Southall Freeman). *George Washington,* Vol. vii, p. 617. Eyre & Spottiswoode, London 1957.

CHAPTER XIII

THE LIFE AND DEATH OF ROBERT BURNS

IT is an interesting phenomenon that the popular Scottish national festival should be the birthday of a poet, not a Saint's day nor the anniversary of a battle. What Englishman knows the date on which Milton or Shakespeare was born, or what Frenchman the birthday of Molière or Victor Hugo? It was another Scotsman, Fletcher of Saltoun, who is remembered for one remark: 'If a man were permitted to make all the ballads, he need not care who made the laws of a nation.' And Robert Burns did indeed 'make the ballads of a nation', all of them for a hundred years until we come to the harmless, tuneful banalities of Harry Lauder and Will Fyfe.

Burns was much more than a poet – he was a national figure, like Bruce and Wallace, and helped to keep Scotland a nation; for in the eighteenth century Scotland, having lost her own King in 1603 and her own Parliament in 1707 was, after the suppression of the '45 rebellion, in danger of becoming a mere province of England under the name of North Britain. John Wilkes, in his political journal *The North Briton*, attacked not only Lord Bute, Prime Minister and favourite of King George III, but the whole Scottish connexion. Burns, as Lord Rosebery once said, was 'both Jacobite and Jacobin', and 'Scots wha hae'' and 'A Man's a Man for a' that' gave Scotland rallying songs that were on every lip. He lived through the time of the French Revolution and he was a born rebel – not always very discreet in what he said and wrote. The words he wrote indelibly with a diamond on the window of the Golden Lion Hotel in Stirling –

'The injured Stuart's line are gone
A race outlandish fill their throne –
An idiot race, to honour lost;
Who know them best, despise them most –'

were written about the Royal Family in whose customs service
Burns was a lowly but ambitious official. The verse was unkind as
well, for King George III was in the midst of his first known attack
of insanity, but in excuse it may be noted that it was written 'on
seeing the royal palace of the Stuarts in ruin', at Stirling Castle.

Burns's revolutionary politics got him into trouble with his
superiors, the Commissioners of Excise. In February 1792, as an
exciseman, he led a boarding party on to an armed smuggling
vessel in the Solway Firth. The ship was condemned, its contents
sold, and Burns bought four carronades for £3, sending them as a
gift to the French legislative body. War with France was not
declared until January 1793, but the guns were intercepted at the
custom-house at Dover, and the Excise Board intimated its serious
displeasure.

It has been suggested by many writers about Burns that this
episode destroyed all his hopes for future promotion, and that this
reacted so unfavourably on his mind that his habits then deteriorated
so much that his death was attributable to it. The legend is that he
died an early death of drink and dissipation. Even Sir Walter Scott
wrote: 'It is but too certain, that from the moment his hopes of
promotion were utterly blasted, his tendency to dissipation hurried
him precipitately into those excesses which shortened his life.'

On the contrary, however, his kindly and influential patron,
Mr Graham of Fintry (a connexion of the Duke of Montrose),
intervened on his behalf, and towards the end of 1795 Burns was
employed as an acting Supervisor of Excise, apparently a step to
permanent promotion. He himself wrote then to his frequent
correspondent, Mrs Dunlop, that 'at last his political sins seemed to
be forgiven him'.

II

The popular legend of the unlettered ploughman poet is a complete misconception. Thomas Carlyle mistakenly wrote that Burns was 'without help, without instruction, without model, or with models only of the meanest sort.' Burns was never a ploughman (though he worked on his father's farm) nor was he unlettered. It is true that when he was introduced into literary circles in Edinburgh as 'the ploughman poet' he accepted the designation, but that was merely because he had an astute realization of its publicity value.

Sir Walter Scott, who met him in Edinburgh at an evening party, when he was a lad of 15, wrote of Burns: 'His person was strong and robust; his manners rustic, not clownish; a sort of dignified plainness and simplicity, which received part of its effect, perhaps, from one's knowledge of his extraordinary talents . . . I think his countenance was more massive than it looks in any of the portraits . . . There was a strong expression of sense and shrewdness in all his lineaments; the eye alone, I think, indicated the poetical character and temperament. It was large, and of a dark cast, which glowed (I say literally *glowed*) when he spoke with feeling or interest. I never saw such another eye in a human head, though I have seen the most distinguished men of my time. His conversation expressed perfect self-confidence, without the slightest presumption . . . His dress corresponded with his manner. He was like a farmer dressed in his best to dine with the Laird.'

Burns's father, who spelt his name Burnes or Burness, was a market gardener at Alloway, two miles from Ayr, though later on his ambition to be a farmer elsewhere led him into financial difficulties. He was a religious man of the highest character, who was the author of a little manual of theology, in the form of a dialogue, which he drew up for the use of his children – after his son's death it was printed and published. His portrait is vividly painted in 'The Cotter's Saturday Night'. He had the typical Scottish urge for self-improvement, and at meals is said to have had a book in one hand

and a fork in the other. He belonged, in fact, to that same class of small Scottish farmer or crofter as the Macmillan who came south from Arran to open a bookshop in London and became a publisher – and whose grandson married the daughter of a Duke and became Prime Minister.

Robert Burns was born on 25th January 1759, and had two somewhat interrupted years of schooling under the young parish schoolmaster John Murdoch; he had a smattering of Latin (which he began at the age of six) and a rather better acquaintance with French (which in later days he was inclined to show off) and elementary geometry. But of course, like most original persons, he was largely self-educated. After all, Winston Churchill learned little at school and did not go to a university; and in the current *Who's Who* that aristocratic, cultured and highly successful litterateur Sir Osbert Sitwell describes himself (and no doubt correctly) as educated 'during the holidays from Eton'.

Robert Burns was widely read, but he had to read the books available to him. The first book he ever read, besides schoolbooks, was a *Life of Hannibal* given to him by his schoolmaster, John Murdoch, and he wrote his first poem at the age of 17. It was perhaps natural that he should put on altogether too high a plane such minor poets of the eighteenth century as Allan Ramsay, Fergusson, and Shenstone. Nevertheless, Allan Ramsay's *Tea-table Miscellany* (published in 1724–27 by instalments) was invaluable to him as a guide to versification, as it was 'A collection of choice songs, Scots and English', some by Ramsay himself, some by his friends, some Caroline poems, and some well-known popular ballads and songs. This was, said Burns, his *vade-mecum*; he pored over them, driving his cart or walking to labour, 'song by song, verse by verse'.

The first novel that Burns read was Richardson's *Pamela*, and he had read Locke's *Essay concerning the Human Understanding* before he was 17. Among the miscellaneous reading of this so-called 'unlettered ploughman' was Stackhouse's *History of the Bible*, Salmon's *Geographical Grammar*, Sterne's *Tristram Shandy*, Henry

Mackenzie's sentimental *Man of Feeling*, some plays of Shakespeare, the poems of Pope and Gray, Young's *Night Thoughts* and Macpherson's *Ossian*.

Burns had almost too much, not too little education, and might easily have developed into a political pamphleteer and a mere editor of other people's poems, except for that undoubted spark of genius that was born in him. Through a friend and admirer, Mr Peter Miller of Dalswinton, Mr Perry, proprietor of the London *Morning Chronicle*, offered Burns a post on the salaried staff of that newspaper. But he replied that because of his family he dared not give up his prospects in the excise, though he promised to send occasional contributions without, however, any payment except a copy of the newspaper.

The poems of Burns cover an amazingly wide range of human experience: love songs, drinking songs, humorous songs, sentimental songs, patriotic songs, charming descriptive verses, witty satirical verse, fantasy, and violent political diatribes. He had a gift for the unforgettable phrase: 'The best laid schemes o' mice and men gang oft agley', 'O wad some Power the giftie gie us to see oursels as others see us', 'Facts are chiels that winna ding', 'Man's inhumanity to man', 'The glorious privilege of being independent', and many another. He often wedded to old lilting traditional tunes words of incomparable beauty. 'My poetry,' he wrote to his good friend Mrs Dunlop, 'is the result of easy composition but of laborious correction.' Part of his genius was a phenomenal memory: Burns has a vocabulary of some 13,000 words, the same number as Milton, who had the advantage of a prolonged classical education at Cambridge and was Cromwell's Latin (i.e. Foreign) Secretary, though many fewer than Shakespeare. It is true that he had what a recent biographer, Mr Hilton Brown, has called 'an unfortunate gift for procreation', but he could never have written his love songs if he had not been a lover. His vivid imagination (his brother Gilbert tells us) made him see a goddess in every girl whom he approached. He wrote at the age of 24 in his 'Commonplace Book' (which is printed in full in the *Reliques*) that 'I never had the least thought or inclination of turning poet till I got once heartily in love, and then rhyme and song were, in a manner, the spontaneous language of my heart'.

Yet the man was even more wonderful than his works. Principal Robertson of Edinburgh University, a famous historian of the day (known to us by one of Raeburn's finest portraits) said of Burns, whom he met more than once: 'His poems had surprised him; his prose compositions appeared even more wonderful; but his conversation was a marvel beyond all.' The Duchess of Gordon once said that Burns was the only man 'whose conversation had carried her off her feet'.

III

Burns's father moved from Alloway to an unsuccessful farm at Mount Oliphant and then, when Burns was 18, on to another at Lochlea, where he remained for seven years. At Tarbolton, the village near Lochlea, Burns became initiated into Freemasonry, which was to be an important influence in his life, and also formed, with his younger brother Gilbert and a few friends, the Bachelors' Club of Tarbolton; it met once a month, a subject was announced for discussion, and not more than threepence was allowed to be spent on refreshment. The ungrateful soil of Lochlea drove Burns to work for a time as a flax-dresser at the small port of Irvine, where he lived (as poor Scots students did still, a century later) mainly on oatmeal supplied by his family. Then after the death of his father came a move to the farm of Mossgiel, near Mauchline, when Burns was 25. Mossgiel was a joint enterprise of the whole family, and the four years there were the most important of his life, when, as Lockhart writes, 'his genius developed its brightest energies'.

The wit and the satirical verses of Burns at Masonic meetings and debating clubs at Mauchline made his name well known in the neighbourhood. 'The Twa Herds' and 'Holy Willie's Prayer', anti-calvinistic satires in verse, spread his fame, and the satirical 'Death and Doctor Hornbook' was written and recited early in 1785. Mossgiel belonged to the Earl of Loudoun, and was held on a sublease from Gavin Hamilton, a lawyer, who became friendly with the poet.

At Mossgiel Burns had a serious illness, and wrote in his 'Commonplace Book': 'A prayer, when fainting fits and other alarming symptoms of a Pleurisy, or some other dangerous disorder which indeed still threaten me, first put Nature on the alarm.' This farm could at best furnish a poor livelihood to so large a family, and Burns, having (as was not unusual in rural Scotland even later than the eighteenth century) got a neighbouring young woman into trouble, but was unacceptable to her father, began to look abroad. At that time, in the plantations of the West Indies, most of the managers or overseers were Scotsmen of the farming class, and one of Burns's friends at Irvine procured for him the post of assistant-overseer on an estate in Jamaica belonging to a Dr Douglas. The passage money was nine guineas, and to raise this Burns had the idea of publishing a collection of his poems in a volume by subscription. Gavin Hamilton and other friends encouraged him, and he entered into an agreement with John Wilson, a printer in the neighbouring town of Kilmarnock. The volume was published successfully in 1786, 612 copies being printed, bringing the author a profit of £20. It contained 'The Twa Dogs', 'The Cotter's Saturday Night', 'To a mouse', 'To a mountain daisy', and other Scottish lyrics.

His sea chest was actually on the way to Greenock, when the Rev Dr Laurie, minister of Loudoun, from whom Burns had received many kindnesses, received an enthusiastic letter about the volume of poems from the Rev Dr Thomas Blacklock of Edinburgh. 'Dr Blacklock,' said Burns, 'belonged to a set of critics for whose applause I had not dared to hope.' Dr Samuel Johnson wrote to Mrs Thrale (17th August 1773) about him: 'This morning I saw at breakfast Dr Blacklock, the blind poet, who does not remember to have seen light, and is read to by a poor scholar in Latin, Greek, and French . . . I looked on him with reverence.'

Burns began to anticipate a more exciting future than the West

Indies could hold. A lively interest in the fortunes of the poet was excited among the gentlefolk in the district where he lived, among them Professor Dugald Stewart of Edinburgh University and Dr Hugh Blair, who was visiting the professor. Mrs Dunlop of Dunlop, a daughter of Sir Thomas Wallace, Bart. (said to have been a descendant of William Wallace, the Scottish patriot), came across a copy of the volume of poems, sent at once to Mossgiel, sixteen miles away, for six more copies, and asked Robert Burns to call on her.

The poet was encouraged to go to Edinburgh, where Dr John Mackenzie of Mauchline and other Ayrshire Masonic friends gave him useful introductions. The Earl of Glencairn persuaded William Creech, the leading Edinburgh bookseller and publisher, to undertake the publication of a second ('Edinburgh') edition of the poems in 1787, and the Hon. Henry Erskine, dean of the Faculty of Advocates, took the poet under his wing. Literary circles in Edinburgh welcomed, lionized, and patronized him. The new volume was, by the interest of Lord Glencairn, dedicated to the Caledonian Hunt, a club of the leading Scottish sporting aristocrats, and the subscription lists were soon filled. There were 1,500 subscribers, and 2,800 copies were printed. It realized between £400 and £500 for the poet (though he had to dun Creech for the last of the proceeds), and he went for two long tours to explore the beauties of Scotland, one to the Border towns, and the other up the eastern Highlands and as far as Inverness.

For six weeks of the winter that Burns spent in Edinburgh he was laid up in his room because of an injury to his knee from the overturning of a hackney coach. He had been invited on the next day to tea, for the first time, by Mrs McLehose ('Clarinda'), and had written accepting it. This was the beginning of a flowery and eventually passionate correspondence, and it is doubtful whether the friendship that ensued was entirely platonic. It inspired, however, that most beautiful of love songs, 'Ae fond kiss'.

'I am here,' he wrote to his correspondent, Miss Chalmers, on 12th December 1787, 'under the care of a surgeon, with a bruised limb extended on a cushion; and the tints of my mind vying with the livid horrors preceding a midnight thunderstorm. A drunken coachman was the cause of the first, and incomparably the lightest evil; misfortune, bodily constitution, hell and myself, have formed a "Quadruple Alliance" to guarantee the other. I got my fall on Saturday, and am getting slowly better.'

The famous Dr Gregory (of 'Gregory's powder'), who had become friendly with the poet, called into consultation 'Lang Sandy' Wood, the leading surgeon of Edinburgh, and he, happening to hear Burns mention his hope for an appointment in the excise, wrote to his friend Mr Graham of Fintry, one of the Commissioners of Excise. Mr Graham had already met Burns at the Duke of Atholl's and had been impressed by his intelligence, so arranged to have his name put on the roll of excise officers.

IV

Burns lent his brother Gilbert £180 'to save Mossgiel', the family farm, and then, in 1788, he married his old sweetheart, Jean Armour, 'before the Sheriff' and took the farm of Ellisland with 172 acres. Ellisland is beautifully situated on the Nith, opposite the estate of Dalswinton, about six miles above Dumfries, but 'it was a poet's choice rather than a farmer's' and the enterprise was a failure; it was not helped by Burns falling from a horse, injuring his arm and hand, and a few months later breaking an arm. 'The implements with which he tilled his land were primitive and clumsy, and his own knowledge of the management of crops exceedingly limited. He plodded on in the regular slothful routine of his ancestors . . . he drained not, neither did he enclose', wrote Alexander Cunningham, father of the poet Allan Cunningham, who was the steward at Dalswinton. Nevertheless, it was at Ellisland that Burns wrote 'Tam o' Shanter', 'John Anderson my Jo', and 'Auld Lang Syne'

In 1789 Burns was appointed exciseman of his district at a salary of £50 a year, but after the failure of his farming he was relieved of the lease of the farm, and in 1791 moved as a full-time exciseman to Dumfries at £70 a year. It should be remembered, however, that there were also perquisites, such as half the amount of fines and confiscations, and that at this period in Scotland the parish schoolmaster was paid £20 a year and the parish minister £35 a year. At Dumfries he lived with his family in comparative comfort; he kept a servant, and had his own small study, with a considerable library. He became a Freeman of the town, and so had the privilege of having his children educated free. But the town of Dumfries in those days was built on a swamp, the rheumatism from which he suffered was aggravated, his temper grew sourer, his political opinions became more embittered, and polite society began to avoid him.

In his youth Burns must have had years of hard work in all weathers and of prolonged malnutrition, for the Scottish traditional staple of oatmeal porridge is now recognized as deficient in vitamins and other essentials, only redeemed when taken with a sufficiency of milk. In 1784 he wrote in his 'Commonplace Book': 'There was a certain period of my life that my spirit was broke by repeated losses and disasters, which threatened, and indeed effected, the utter ruin of my fortune. My body too was attacked by that most dreadful distemper, a hypochondria, or confirmed melancholy: In this wretched state, the recollection of which makes me yet shudder, I hung my harp on the willow trees.'

On 31st December 1792, he wrote to Mrs Dunlop: 'As to myself, I am better, though not quite free of my complaint. – You must not think, as you seem to insinuate, that in my way of life I want exercise. Of that I have enough; but occasional hard drinking is the devil to me. Against this I have again and again bent my resolution, and have greatly succeeded. Taverns I have totally abandoned: it is the private parties in the family way, among the hard drinking gentlemen of this country, that do me the mischief – but even this, I have more than half given over.'

A later letter to Mrs Dunlop is dated, Castle Douglas, 25th June 1794: 'To tell you that I have been in poor health, will not be excuse enough, though it is true. I am afraid I am about to suffer for the follies of my youth. My medical friends threaten me with a flying gout; but I trust they are mistaken.'

V

The first *Life* of Burns, written by Dr James Currie of Liverpool, was published, with his *Works*, in four volumes in 1800. Dr Currie was without experience of editing (although he published a volume of *Medical Reports* in 1798) and was full of prejudices, a fanatical teetotaller, a man of high principles, but of censorious disposition, who had no compunction in altering facts to suit his thesis. It is he who is chiefly responsible for the persistence of the story of Burns's drunkenness and profligacy. Currie was born and educated in Scotland, then had a chequered career in America, until he graduated M.D. at Edinburgh in 1780. He went into medical practice in Liverpool and prospered so well that he bought an estate in Dumfriesshire, where he met Burns briefly in 1792. He offered his services as biographer and editor for the benefit of the widow and children of Burns, without remuneration to himself. He wrote of Burns as follows: 'Upwards of a year before his death, there was an evident decline in our poet's personal appearance, and though his appetite continued unimpaired, he was himself sensible that his constitution was sinking ... His temper now became more irritable and gloomy; he fled from himself into society, often of the lowest kind. And in such company that part of the convivial scene, in which wine increases sensibility and excites benevolence, was hurried over, to reach the succeeding part, over which uncontrolled passion generally presided. He who suffers the pollution of inebriation, how shall he escape other pollution?'

For this last unkind suggestion of Dr Currie's, there is no evidence whatever. Burns's sweethearts had been country girls, not women of the town, and he showed no signs of disease. James Gray, who had been the teacher of Burns's children at the local grammar school and knew the poet well, wrote after his death: 'Nor was there any decay in any of the power of his mind. To the last day of his life, his judgement, his memory, his imagination, were fresh and vigorous as when he composed *The Cotter's Saturday Night*. The truth is, that Burns was seldom intoxicated.'

And his immediate superior in the Dumfries excise district, Mr Findlater, wrote (quoted by Lockhart): 'I never saw his spirit fail till he was borne down by the pressure of disease and bodily weakness; and even then it would occasionally revive, and, like an expiring lamp, emit bright flashes to the last.'

Professor Dugald Stewart wrote to Dr Currie when he was preparing his *Life*: 'He told me, indeed, himself, that the weakness of his stomach was such as to deprive him entirely of any merit in his temperance. I was, however, somewhat alarmed about the effect of his now comparatively sedentary and luxurious life, when he confessed to me, the first night he spent in my house after his writer's campaign in town, that he had been much disturbed when in bed by a palpitation at his heart, which, he said, was a complaint to which he had of late become subject.'

In the autumn of 1795 his only daughter died, and he became the victim of severe rheumatic fever. There is a story, long current, that Burns, when coming very late from dining and drinking at the Globe Tavern, fell asleep in the snow, returning home 'benumbed and intoxicated', the attack of rheumatic fever following. But it is now known that he was ill in bed at this time and could not have visited the tavern. He wrote of this illness: 'After many weeks of a sick-bed . . . I am beginning to crawl across the room.'

His appetite now began to fail, his hand shook, his voice faltered on any exertion or emotion. His pulse became weaker and more rapid, and pain in the larger joints, and in the hands and feet, deprived him of refreshing sleep. He became weak and emaciated, and in June 1796, his doctor, Dr William Maxwell of Dumfries, advised him to go to the country, to a little village spa twenty miles away on the Solway Firth called Brow Well, which had an iron spring, and there have daily sea-bathing and regular exercise on horseback. As instructed, he drank the iron waters, and each day he waded a long way out in the shallow, muddy waters of the Solway Firth, until the chilly sea-water reached his armpits (for sea-bathing, in the reign of King George III, had become the fashion, though usually in a more southern and salubrious clime). He had no money to spare for horseback riding. Then he went back to his lodging and sipped his due allowance of port wine.

From Brow Well he wrote to his friend Alexander Cunningham: 'Alas! my friend, I fear the voice of the Bard will soon be heard among you no more! For these eight or ten months I have been ailing, sometimes bedfast and sometimes not; but these last three months I have been tortured with an excruciating rheumatism, which has reduced me to nearly the last stave. – You actually would not know if you saw me. – Pale, emaciated and so feeble as occasionally to need help from my chair – my spirits fled! but I can no more on the subject – only the medical folk tell me that my last and only chance is bathing and country quarters and riding.'

At first poor Burns thought that the sea-bathing relieved the pains in his limbs, but this was followed by a new attack of fever. He survived the régime for a month and then, worried about some quite trivial debts, he drove home to Dumfries in a borrowed gig on 18th July. He was too weak to go upstairs to his bedroom, so he collapsed into the kitchen box-bed, where he died four days later, on 21st July 1796.

VI

Sir James Crichton-Browne, an eminent if opinionated physician and psychiatrist, who was a native of Dumfries, insisted that Burns died of endocarditis, a disease of the substance and lining membrane of the heart. 'It is characteristic,' he wrote, 'of the mild types of this insidious form of heart disease from which Burns suffered, that its victims, until it is far advanced, are able to go about and take an active share in affairs, as if there was nothing the matter with them. But they are visited at different intervals during its course of 20 or

o

30 years by feverish attacks, significant often of another milestone on the downward journey, in which, with a quickened pulse, they become weak and qualmish, and are highly strung, nervous and easily agitated. It is attacks of this kind that are occasionally tabulated in Burns's correspondence . . . It will not, I think, be disputed that Burns died of rheumatic endocarditis.'

Dr S. Watson Smith of Bournemouth, a specialist in rheumatism who was once President of the British Medical Association, wrote in 1944 that 'alcoholic excess and rheumatic fever, even an "accidental disease" (i.e. venereal disease) have been put forward as the cause of Burns's death and such assertions have been uncritically repeated from book to book . . . Burns's last long illness, extending over many months, gradually worsening, was certainly not the result of rheumatic fever. To modern medical thought and beliefs the description of the nature and course of his disease, scant as it is and necessarily would be, indicates that he suffered and died from subacute infective endocarditis – that microbic inflammation of the heart which has a usual fatal ending in septicaemia. In this condition a painful arthritis is not a rare complication. The anxiety and dreadful suspense that assailed the sick poet at the last would, more likely than alcoholism, dispose to the particular disease.'

Following Dr Watson Smith's article in the *British Medical Journal*, Dr Letitia Fairfield, a learned physician with literary connexions, suggested quite bluntly that the immediate cause of Burns's death was actually the treatment recommended by his doctor – the sea-bathing, exercise on horseback, glasses of port wine and iron water.

It is true that while this treatment was unsuitable in a relapse, it was probably well enough indicated – according to the accepted medical practice of the day – before Burns left Dumfries for the Solway Firth. Certainly it was not drink nor dissipation that killed Robert Burns at the age of 37. Alcohol probably prolonged his life. But it should be remembered that in 1796 medical science was still in the dark ages, before the 'germ theory' of disease had been suspected, and before even the stethoscope or the clinical thermometer had been invented.

At once, when the poet had been buried with an elaborate funeral procession and a military firing party over his grave, a fund was raised for his family that soon reached £1,200. Currie's four-volume edition of his poems brought in £1,400 and a continued income, and when, some years later, his widow was given a Civil List pension, she was able to refuse it after only one payment. His eldest son was appointed to the Stamp Office in London, the second died young, and the two youngest had successful careers with the East India Company.

REFERENCES

The Works of Robert Burns; with an account of his life, by J. Currie, 4 vols. Cadell, London; and Creech, Edinburgh 1800.

Reliques of Robert Burns, ed. by R. H. Cromek, Cadell, London 1808.

J. G. LOCKHART. *Life of Robert Burns*, John Murray, London 1828.

SIR JAMES CRICHTON-BROWNE. *Burns From a New Point of View*, Hodder & Stoughton, London 1926.

J. D. L. FERGUSSON. *The Letters of Robert Burns*, Clarendon Press, Oxford 1931.

S. WATSON SMITH. *The disease that killed Robert Burns*. British Medical Journal, 1944, Vol. *ii*, p. 864.

LETITIA FAIRFIELD. *Death of Robert Burns*. British Medical Journal, 1945, Vol. *i*, p. 98.

HILTON BROWN. *There was a Lad*, H. Hamilton, London 1949.

DAVID DAICHES. *Robert Burns*, Bell, London 1952.

ESTHER H. VINCENT. *Robert Burns and his heart*. Surgery, Gynecology and Obstetrics, 1954, Vol. **99**, p. 245.

A. L. GOODALL. *Robert Burns and the Medical Profession*. Scottish Medical Journal, 1959, Vol. **4**, p. 133.

CHAPTER XIV

THE MEDICAL HISTORY
OF QUEEN ANNE

THE reign of Queen Anne is one of the glorious periods of British history, memorable for the victories of Marlborough and the capture of Gibraltar, the Augustan Age of English literature, the formation of the English political party system, some of the best English architecture, and the beginnings of the English school of painting. Swift and Defoe, Steele and Addison laid the foundations of modern English prose, and their contemporaries Pope and Congreve lent lustre to poetry and the drama; Hogarth was the first native English painter of importance, for Holbein, Van Dyke, Lely and Kneller were all foreigners; Purcell's opera, *The Fairy Queen*, was produced in 1692; the first daily newspaper, the *Daily Courant*, began in 1702; Vanburgh built his palaces and Sir Christopher Wren finished St Paul's Cathedral; Grinling Gibbons carved and sculpted; and although Sir Isaac Newton, greatest of English natural philosophers, was president of the Royal Society in the reign of Charles II, it was Queen Anne who knighted him.

Yet Queen Anne herself was ill-educated, 'ignorant in everything but what the parsons had taught her as a child', and a self-indulgent, gross woman, who habitually over-ate (though there is no real evidence that she also tippled), spent her evenings playing cards – basset and ombre, at which she gambled heavily, was interested only in trivialities such as rules of precedence and fashions, and was completely dominated for over 26 years by a jealous and ambitious woman friend, Sarah, duchess of Marlborough, with whom the relationship was at least equivocal. Queen Anne's choice of Ministers was influenced entirely by personal likes and dislikes, but the effect of sovereignty then was such that they accepted her insistence on presiding at their Councils. She had a sweet speaking voice, for her intelligent uncle Charles II had had her trained in elocution by the celebrated actress Mrs Betterton, but except for her devotion to her own particular high church faction of the Church of England, she had no other virtues whatever.

II

The Princess Anne (who became Queen in 1702) was born in 1665, the second surviving daughter of James, duke of York (afterwards King James II) by his first wife, Anne Hyde, daughter of the earl of Clarendon. She was a delicate child, had smallpox when she was 12, and her habitual frown was due not to bad temper but to inflammation of the eyes and resultant shortsightedness. By the express command of King Charles II and with the consent of their father, Anne and her elder sister Mary were brought up as members of the Church of England. The two sisters apparently both expected to succeed to the throne in turn, and encouraged the doubts regarding their brother James, 'the Old Pretender'.

In 1683, at the age of 18, the Princess Anne married Prince George of Denmark, who was tall, fair, corpulent, and asthmatic. Charles II remarked of him, 'I've tried George drunk and I've tried him sober, and there's nothing in him'. His virtue, however, was that he was a Protestant, a Lutheran, and a faithful husband to Anne, despite being not infrequently drunk. He probably knew nothing about the disease from which he must have suffered (and which may have been congenital). For the Princess Anne had 17 pregnancies, many of them ending in miscarriage, and only one of her children survived more than a few days or weeks. This boy, the duke of Gloucester, a sickly child with 'water on the brain', or hydrocephalus, died at the age of 11. The only possible explanation for such a long series of disasters is that the husband was syphilitic and the 'water on the brain' was due to a low-grade syphilitic meningitis. It is hardly surprising however, that such a history of miscarriages and stillbirths made Anne into a virtual invalid by the time she was 30.

King James II succeeded his brother in 1685 without public enthusiasm but without opposition, and at once pledged himself to the Privy Council to preserve the laws of England and protect its Church. As Duke of York he had begun to turn towards Roman Catholicism and had even inquired whether he could obtain a papal dispensation to remain outwardly a Protestant after joining the Church of Rome, but Pope Clement IX refused. He became a convert to Roman Catholicism after the death in 1671 of his duchess, Anne Hyde, who had already been converted, and his subsequent marriage to the Italian Princess Mary of Modena confirmed him in his new faith.

King James had all the fervency of a convert, and when he came to the throne one stupidity after another turned the country, which had been flooded by Protestant refugees from France after the Edict of Nantes, against him: the Bloody Assize of Judge Jefferies, the trial and acquittal of the seven Bishops for 'seditious libel', the admission and promotion of numerous Roman Catholics to high rank in the Army, the appointment of well-known Roman Catholics as Viceroy of Ireland and High Commissioner in Scotland, as Dean of Christ Church at Oxford, and the dismissal of the Vice-Chancellor of Cambridge for refusing to violate his statutes by granting a degree to a monk.

On the day of the acquittal of the seven bishops, William of Orange (who had married his cousin Mary, elder daughter of James II) was invited by 'seven influential Englishmen' to come to England. The invitation was urgent because of the possibility of a Roman Catholic dynasty, for King James's Queen had given birth to a son in June 1688. The birth gave rise to fantastic stories of substitution and impersonation, which were eagerly accepted by the populace, though the 'warming-pan' legend was mere propaganda invented by a notorious rogue and swindler named William Fuller.

On 5th November William of Orange landed at Torbay. It was soon evident that the country welcomed him, Prince George of Denmark and Marlborough being among the first people to do so, and on 22nd December King James II left England for ever. Next year and in 1690 his disastrous campaign in Ireland saw his last hopes disappear, and the position of William was firmly consolidated. Queen Mary, the elder daughter of James II, was heir to the throne, but she refused to have her husband merely as a consort and insisted that William III must share the sovereignty and be recognized as heir in his own right.

King William was a wise and far-seeing statesman, aiming at a balance of power by combining Holland and England against France, but he was not very clever at managing Parliament. Marlborough, after his successes in Ireland, was disappointed in not being given office in the government, and had some communication with the exiled James II. As a result King William dismissed him in 1692 from his Army command and from the Court, thus precipitating a quarrel not only with the Marlboroughs but with Princess Anne. But when Queen Mary died suddenly from smallpox in December 1694, King William made his peace with Anne, who was now heir apparent, and handed over St James's Palace to her.

In 1702, while riding in the park at Hampton Court one afternoon in March, William was making his horse change from a walk to a gallop when it put a foot into a molehill and fell on its knees. The king fell forward on to his right shoulder, broke his collar-bone, caught a chill, developed pneumonia, and died a fortnight later, at the age of 51.

III

On her marriage the Princess Anne was given an establishment of her own, a suite of apartments in the rambling palace of Whitehall at 'The Cockpit', on the site of which Downing Street now stands. Mrs Churchill was appointed a lady of the bedchamber to the Princess, though the 'first lady' was the countess of Clarendon, her aunt by marriage, 'who looked like a mad-woman and talked like a scholar'.

Sarah Jennings, now Mrs Churchill, had played with the Princess Anne since childhood, though Sarah was four years the elder. She was a maid-of-honour to the duchess of York, Anne's stepmother, and in 1678 she married handsome Colonel John Churchill, who some years before had captured for a time the wayward fancy of Charles II's duchess of Cleveland; she gave the penniless young officer £5,000, with which at once he rather cold-bloodedly purchased an annuity. Sarah Churchill was tall and slender, with dark blue eyes and honey-coloured hair, but with a quick temper and a sharp tongue; she and her husband were devoted to each other until he died in 1722.

The Princess Anne found young Mrs Churchill much more agreeable than the countess of Clarendon, and when Lord Clarendon was appointed Viceroy of Ireland Mrs Churchill became her first lady of the bedchamber. The two friends began to find 'Your Royal Highness' and other forms of ceremonial address increasingly uneasy, and the Princess suggested one day that they should call each other in their letters Mrs Morley and Mrs Freeman, assuming the former for herself. It was not, indeed, unusual at this period for friends when writing to use similar names for each other and sometimes numerals or cyphers when referring to other persons, for the post was by no means certain or secret, and letters might well be opened and read.

'The Queen's letters,' wrote the duchess of Marlborough, 'were very indifferent, both in sense and spelling, unless they were generally enlivened with a few passionate expressions, sometimes pretty enough, but repeated over and over again, without the mixture either of diversion or instruction.

'Her friendships were flames of extravagant passion, ending in indifference or aversion; her love to the prince seemed, in the eyes of the world, to be prodigiously great; but great as was the passion of grief, her stomach was greater.

'I know that in some libels she has been reproached as one who indulged herself in drinking strong liquors, but I believe this to be entirely groundless, and that she never went beyond such a quantity of strong wines as her physicians judged to be necessary for her.

'She loved fawning and adoration, and hated plain dealing, even in the most important cases. She had a soul that nothing could so effectually move as flattery or fear.'

As the friendship developed, Anne's manner became more and more humble towards her increasingly arrogant favourite, and when she was absent the Princess wrote to her four or five times every day. In thanking her for a trinket she wrote: 'Ten thousand thanks for the dear ring which methinks is very pretty. When I have once got it on my finger we will never part – and oh that my dear Mrs Freeman would imagine how much I value any mark of her favour – but that's impossible.'

When Marlborough was in disfavour with King William III, the Princess wrote to Sarah: 'I gave dear Mrs Freeman a thousand thanks for her kind letter, which gives me an account of her concerns; and that is what I desire more to know than any other news. . . . I confess, I long to see you, but am not so unreasonable to desire that satisfaction till it is easy to you. I wish with all my soul, that you may not be a true prophetess, and that it may be soon in our power to enjoy one another's company, more than it has been of late; which is all I covet in this world.' Again: 'And there is no misery I cannot readily resolve to suffer, rather than the thought of parting from you. And I do swear, I would sooner be torn in pieces, than alter this my resolution. My dear Mrs Freeman, I long to hear from you.'

Another letter ends: 'Dear Mrs Freeman farewell. I hope in Christ you will never think more of leaving me, for I would be sacrificed to do you the least service, and nothing but death can ever make me part with you. For if it be possible I am every day more and more yours.'

When Queen Anne succeeded to the throne in 1702 the earl of

Marlborough received the Garter and was made Captain-General of the Army at home and abroad, and Ranger of Windsor Park (which gave him a very pleasant residence there). After his successful campaign in the first year of Queen Anne's reign he was created a duke. In the letter that the queen wrote to his wife to say that she intended to make Marlborough a duke, she ended: 'It does not enough express the value I have for Mrs Freeman, nor ever can how passionately I am yours, my dear Mrs Freeman.' Lady Marlborough became Groom of the Stole, Mistress of the Robes, controlled the privy purse, and prepared herself to rule imperiously over the Court and its appointments.

Later on, the duchess extracted a promise from the queen that her offices would be transferred to her daughters, but she began to suspect that it would not be fulfilled. Influenced by repeated importunities, her husband was persuaded to approach the queen on the subject, but she tactfully put him off. When, however, the duchess later asked the queen whether the duke had understood her correctly the queen answered, 'I desire that I may never be troubled any more on the subject'.

After the victory of Malplaquet in 1709 Marlborough suggested to the queen that she should make him Captain-General of her armies for life, 'intimating that the War would probably last not only the duration of their lives, but probably for ever'. But Queen Anne was longing for peace, lamenting the heavy losses in Marlborough's hard-won victories, and prudently referred the request to the Lord Chancellor, Lord Cowper, who told Marlborough that 'he would never put the Great Seal of England to any such commission', and the suggestion was dropped.

The duchess of Marlborough had made one fatal mistake. In or about 1698 she had introduced an impoverished cousin, Abigail Hill, as woman of the bedchamber to the Princess Anne. Sarah and Abigail had a mutual grandfather, but he had 24 children, so that each had only a tiny inheritance. Sarah took Abigail into her household at St Albans, where she lived with her and her children; and when there was a vacancy as bedchamber woman she asked the princess to give it to Abigail, whom she considered unattractive – but she was highly intelligent.

There is a story, mentioned even by Voltaire, that some quarrel about a pair of gloves ended the friendship of Queen Anne and the duchess of Marlborough. Miss Agnes Strickland gives it in more detail. One afternoon, not long after the death of the little duke of Gloucester, Abigail Hill went to fetch the Princess Anne's gloves, which she had left in the next room. Lady Marlborough was sitting reading a letter and had accidentally put on the Princess's gloves by mistake. Abigail mentioned the mistake to her and Sarah pulled off the gloves, exclaiming irritably, 'Have I on anything that has touched the odious hands of that disagreeable woman. Take them away!' The door was ajar and the princess had heard every word quite plainly, but the incident remained a profound secret between her and Abigail Hill.

The duchess had no suspicions of her cousin Abigail until news reached her of her secret marriage to Samuel Masham, a groom of the bedchamber to Prince George, in the summer of 1707. She soon discovered, as she wrote in her memoir, that 'her cousin was become an absolute favourite, that the Queen herself was present at her marriage in Dr Arbuthnot's lodgings, at which time Her Majesty had called for a round sum out of the privy purse; that Mrs Masham came often to the queen when the prince was asleep, and was generally two hours every day in private with her'.

After the death of Prince George, the queen, 'not caring to have it known how much time she passed with Mrs Masham', ordered fires to be lit in two small closets that had been used by the prince. These unattractive rooms, which looked out into an ugly, enclosed little space used for drying linen, communicated with a waiting-room beside the queen's dressing-room, but had also backstairs which went down to Mrs Masham's lodgings, so that Mrs Masham could go privately to the queen.

The final break with the duchess of Marlborough came in 1710.

On 3rd April the duchess waited on the queen and asked for a private audience, suggesting various times, and at length was told to present herself at six o'clock on the following evening, the hour usually set aside for the royal devotions. But she was again put off, and was asked to make her communication in writing. The duchess wrote a letter to the queen, but without waiting for a reply went to Kensington and sent a page of the backstairs to let the queen know that she was there. When she was admitted, the queen appeared to be embarrassed and said, 'I was just going to write to you', and, as the duchess was about to speak, added, 'whatever you have to say, you may put it in writing'. 'Indeed,' protested the duchess, 'I can't tell how to put such things in writing.' The queen replied, 'you may put it in writing', and in reply to the protests of the duchess repeated this sentence over and over again.

The duchess urged that her reply should be heard to the calumnies with which she believed that she had been assailed. But the queen turned aside and answered briefly, 'there are many lies told'. The duchess continued to protest, but the queen said, 'I will give you no answer'. She moved towards the door, and the duchess followed, bursting into a flood of tears, making further protests. After another flood of tears the duchess exclaimed, 'I am confident you will suffer in this world or the next for so much inhumanity'. The queen answered, 'that is my business', and left the room. After this long and tempestuous scene all personal intercourse was broken off, though publicly the duke and duchess were still honoured by the queen, who apparently feared recriminations, for the duchess threatened to publish her letters.

To a modern medical psychologist with any experience of sex problems the picture presented is that of a typical lesbian relationship: the weak and wealthy woman dominated for years by an unscrupulous stronger character, the ceaseless correspondence with constant endearing terms, then the appearance of a new woman friend, the subsequent desperate quarrels about nothing and the floods of tears, and then the feelings of absolute aversion, with fears that compromising letters might be made public. It is not possible to be certain today about the relationship, but the inaccessible private archives of Blenheim Palace may well contain the evidence.

Lesbianism is a very inclusive term, and ranges from fondling and embracing (with an element of sex in it) to actual sexual perversions such as cunnilingus and tribadism. To a much greater extent than in the male it can exist along with heterosexual behaviour. Sometimes it is the expression of deep and genuine affection, sometimes of mere perverted sexual gratification. But it is neither congenital nor inherited, nor is it due to some endocrine ('gland') disorder; it is a behaviour symptom of a deep-seated neurosis. It is more common than is often imagined, although Henderson and Gillespie, for instance – and they are not alone – in their standard *Textbook of Psychiatry,** seem unaware of its existence and devote their chapter on homosexuality entirely to the male. In her book on *Factors in the sex life of 2,200 women*, Dr Katherine B. Davis found 450 admitting 'overt' homosexual experience; and Dr Kinsey found 28 per cent of homosexual contacts among the females in the (rather restricted) group that he studied. It must be remembered that lesbianism, unlike male homosexuality, is not a criminal offence in the eyes of the law.

IV

With her history of frequent miscarriage and stillbirths, it is not surprising that Princess Anne was in a state of constant ill-health and suffering. She became dropsical and a victim of gout, and by the age of 30 had to be carried from one place to another as a cripple. At the state funeral of Queen Mary in 1694 the Princess Anne could not follow as chief mourner, as dropsy made her unable to walk. At her coronation Queen Anne, who was then aged 37, had to be carried in some of the processions in a low armchair, as she had lost the use of her feet 'from gout and corpulence', which made the long

* The 1962 edition does mention 'and women', and gives a reference to Dr Kinsey's book.

ceremonial fatiguing and even embarrassing to her. She had to have the aid of sustaining hands to support her when she was standing, and it was only with the assistance of the Archbishops and the Lord Great Chamberlain that she contrived to reach the altar. (Incidentally, when the coronation was safely over, thieves stole the whole of the plate used at the banquet in Westminster Hall.)

The queen's want of moderation in eating made her relapses very frequent, and she had many attacks of 'gout in the stomach' as well as in her limbs. After being seriously ill with 'gout' in the head or the stomach on a Friday, on the Sunday she would devour a whole fowl as a main dish, besides other dishes before and after.

When stormy debates occurred in Parliament the queen was alarmed lest a disastrous minority would cast her again into the power of the Marlboroughs and their friends, and went into hysterical 'fits'. Occasionally she recovered the use of her feet and limbs, with strength sufficient to allow her to hunt the stag in long hunting drives, which she continued until the summer of 1712. She was very fond of hunting, and followed the chase sometimes for forty miles, not only in a strange equipage with high wheels, but at a strange season – in July, when the harvest was on the ground. Dean Swift, who was a friend of Mrs Abigail Masham and her sister, in his *Journal to Stella* wrote (on 31st July 1711): 'The Queen was abroad today to hunt, but finding it disposed to rain she kept in her coach; she hunts in a chaise with one horse, which she drives herself, and drives furiously like Jehu, and is a mighty hunter like Nimrod.'

From the autumn of 1711 to the summer of 1714 Queen Anne had a long series of relapses into ill-health. In 1713 the queen was seriously ill and could take no further violent exercise. She was reported to have 'gout in her stomach' and had 'a dangerous cough'. 'The gout vibrated fearfully through the Queen's frame,' Swift wrote, 'flying from her feet to her stomach. At last, being carried in an open chair, on the 9th of April, to the House of Lords, Her Majesty pronounced her speech with her usual harmony of utterance, yet it was noted that her voice was weaker than usual.'

By July 1713, it was observed that the queen had swollen to such an enormous degree of corpulence that 'she had not been able to walk a step since the preceding November, and was obliged to be lifted into her coach by a machine that had been constructed for that purpose'. During her stay at Windsor Castle in the autumn and winter of 1713, she was, to spare herself the trouble of ascending and descending stairs, lowered from the ceiling of one room into another, by means of a chair fitted up with pulleys and tackling.

V

At Christmas 1713, Queen Anne fell seriously ill, and was in increasingly bad health for the next seven months, though only a few weeks before her death, Dr Arbuthnot wrote to Dean Swift that the queen 'was in good health'. In July 1714, she was very ill, but was carried down to prorogue Parliament, and insisted on presiding over all the meetings of her Cabinet. A long and stormy Council on the night of 27th July ended at two o'clock in the morning by the Queen collapsing into a dead faint. She was hastily put to bed and spent the night in tears, dreading another stormy Council. She was too ill to attend a Council on the following day, and on the evening of 29th July she was taken with a burning fever and delirium, and a consultation was held in the middle of the night by Dr Arbuthnot and the other royal physicians in ordinary attendance on Her Majesty – Dr Thomas Lawrence, Dr Hans Sloane, Dr Shadwell and Sir David Hamilton.

Dr John Arbuthnot, the Scotsman who was the queen's favourite physician, was educated at Aberdeen and at Oxford and graduated M.D. of St Andrews in 1696. He happened to be present once when Prince George of Denmark was taken ill, and treated him so successfully that Queen Anne appointed him a physician-in-ordinary. He was also a witty Tory pamphleteer, a friend of Swift and Pope, and famous for his 'John Bull' and 'Martin Scriblerus'. He was a firm friend and ally of Abigail Masham.

Dr Thomas Lawrence was 'first physician' to Queen Anne and

Physician General to the Army. He began his career when King Charles II appointed him physician to the garrison at Tangier, and he lived to a ripe old age. Dr Thomas Lawrence, the friend of Samuel Johnson, was his grandson. Dr Hans Sloane (the first medical baronet) was born in Ireland, and accompanied, as his physician, the second Duke of Albemarle to Jamaica when he was appointed Governor. The Duke soon died out there, and Sloane returned to London with a large collection of the flora and fauna of the West Indies. This gave him a taste for collecting, from which arose the foundation of the British Museum.

The physicians in consultation agreed that Queen Anne should be cupped, and this was done about two o'clock in the morning, when eight ounces of blood, 'very thick', were taken from her, which relieved her worst symptoms. But it was observed that her eyes were dull and heavy, and indications of severe indigestion occurred. Indeed, the common story of the day was that Queen Anne 'died from eating a vast quantity of black-heart cherries', which was perhaps not unfounded.

Towards morning the Queen fell asleep, but arose at her usual hour of seven o'clock and was combed and attired by her women attendants, in preparation for a meeting of her Council. At half-past eight, however, she had a relapse, and Dr Arbuthnot was hastily summoned and was forced to make the illness public, 'for he could not have recourse to the lancet without more authority,' and he now considered that his royal patient was suffering 'under an access of apoplexy'. He ordered that the Queen's head should be shaved, and ten ounces of blood were taken from the Queen's arm by her apothecary, Mr Dickens.

Queen Anne remained unconscious for nearly two hours, while the physicians wrangled over her case, politics playing as important a part in it as medicine. Dr Richard Mead demanded that those who were really in favour of the Protestant succession should send notice of Her Majesty's symptoms to the Elector of Hanover and his physicians. Dr Mead had been educated at Leyden, graduated

M.D. at Padua, and returned to practise in London in 1696. He became physician to St Thomas's Hospital in 1703, took over Dr Radcliffe's house in Bloomsbury in 1714, and became the leading physician of the day. It was considered afterwards that the prompt boldness of this political physician largely brought about the peaceful accession of King George I.

On the other hand, Dr Arbuthnot, who was an ardent Jacobite, was in touch with some of the leading Jacobites through Abigail Masham, in whose apartment they held a conference, but decided that nothing could be done without the direct orders of Queen Anne, which was impossible. Dr Arbuthnot held out hopes of her recovery, but Dr Mead predicted that her death was merely a matter of an hour. However, after she had been bled again, Queen Anne recovered enough consciousness to hand the white wand of the office of Lord Treasurer to the Whig Duke of Shrewsbury, as the Privy Council had suggested. The Privy Council then assembled in the royal bedchamber and called on the Queen's physicians to declare their opinions, which were unanimous that the state of the Queen was hopeless.

The Privy Council sent to Carshalton for the famous Dr Radcliffe, but he replied that 'he was ill and had taken physic and could not come'. As a result of his refusal the Queen's death was laid at his door by the public, and he had to brave a storm of unpopularity. Dr John Radcliffe was educated at University College, Oxford, and graduated M.D. of Oxford in 1682. He moved to London in 1684 and was soon very successful. Princess Anne appointed him her principal physician, but quarrelled with him when once he refused to attend her 'as it was nothing but the vapours'. He also offended King William III when he said that 'he would not have the king's two legs for his three kingdoms', and never saw him again. He died unmarried in 1714 and left a large fortune, which provided funds for the building at Oxford of the Radcliffe Infirmary, Observatory and Library, and for two medical travelling fellowships.

After hours of semi-consciousness Queen Anne died at eight

P

o'clock in the morning of Sunday, 1st August 1714, in her fiftieth year. A post-mortem examination next day revealed nothing of importance, the physicians 'being forbid making any other inspection than what was absolutely necessary for embalming the body'.

Later on the Sunday morning the proclamation of King George I took place peacefully, and three days afterwards saw the triumphant re-entry into London of the duke of Marlborough from his voluntary exile abroad, 'attended by hundreds of gentlemen on horseback and some of the nobility in their coaches'. Queen Anne was dead indeed and was buried in a coffin that was almost square.

REFERENCES

SARAH, DUCHESS OF MARLBOROUGH. *An Account of the Conduct of the Dowager Duchess of Marlborough*, George Hawkins, London 1742.

ANON. (known to be Dean Swift). *Memoirs of the Last Four Years of the Reign of Queen Anne*, T. Cooper, London 1742.

WILLIAM COXE. *Memoirs of John Duke of Marlborough*, 3 vols. Longman, London 1818.

Memoirs of John Evelyn, Vol. ii. Edited by William Bray. Colburn, London 1818.

Private Correspondence of Sarah, Duchess of Marlborough, 2 vols. Colburn, London 1838.

AGNES STRICKLAND. *Lives of the Queens of England*, 12 vols. ('Queen Anne' in Vols. II and 12). Colburn, London 1847.

LORD MACAULAY. *History of England from the Accession of James II*, 5 vols. Longmans, London 1849–61.

JOHN ASHTON. *Social Life in the Reign of Queen Anne*, 2 vols. Chatto & Windus, London 1882.

JONATHAN SWIFT. *Journal to Stella* (1710–1713), edited by F. Ryland, Bell, London 1913.

GERTRUDE SCOTT STEVENSON. *The Letters of Madame*, 2 vols. Chapman & Dodd, London 1924; Arrowsmith, 1925.

KATHLEEN CAMPBELL. *Sarah Duchess of Marlborough*, Thornton Butterworth, London 1932.

WINSTON S. CHURCHILL. *Marlborough: his life and times*, 4 vols. Harrap, London 1933–38.

G. N. CLARK. *The Later Stuarts, 1660–1714,* Clarendon Press, Oxford 1934.

D. K. HENDERSON and R. D. GILLESPIE. *Textbook of Psychiatry,* 6th edition. Oxford University Press 1944.

A. C. KINSEY *et al. Sexual behavior in the Human Female,* Saunders, Philadelphia 1953.

SIR EARDLEY HOLLAND and ALECK BOURNE. *British Obstetric and Gynaecological Practice,* Heinemann, London 1955.

FRANK S. CAPRIO. *Female Homosexuality,* Peter Owen, London 1960.

CHAPTER XV

THE DEATHBED OF KING CHARLES II

AFTER the death of Oliver Cromwell, and during the half-hearted, brief régime of his son Richard, cries for the restoration of King Charles II were soon raised. In May 1660, deputations from the Lords, Commons and the City waited upon the exiled monarch at the Hague, and he was welcomed at Dover by Monk, soon to be duke of Albemarle, who controlled the Army.

The new king was tall, dark and vigorous, a good dancer and fond of hunting and horse-racing, and it was said that 'the first years of his reign were a continued jubilee'. His penurious exile had made him easy of access, and he was charming and courteous. He was not particularly well-read, although in the fashion of the day he had a laboratory and knew something of science and mathematics, but he was intelligent and his conversation was full of wit and humour. His character, though, was marred by his detestation of business and his love of pleasure, and his pleasant manners hid a heartless sensuality. The earl of Rochester wrote of him:

> *'Who never said a foolish thing,*
> *Nor ever did a wise one.'*

Lucy Walter (or Walters) is said to have been his first mistress, in Holland when he was aged 18. She was an English refugee of good family, ruined by the Civil War, but Charles was not her first lover, and when he went to Scotland in 1650 she had an intrigue with Colonel Bennet, afterwards Earl of Arlington, so that Charles broke off the connexion on his return. But she was the mother of the boy who became Duke of Monmouth (besides a daughter who married William Sarsfield, a cousin of Lord Lucan), and who was persuaded that King Charles had secretly married his mother and that he was the rightful heir to the throne – but his pretentions ended with Sedgemoor and his execution at the Tower in 1685.

Charles had other mistresses during his exile, Elizabeth Killigrew (Lady Shannon) and Eleanor Needham (Lady Byron), and at the Restoration he brought with him from Holland the fascinating and rapacious Barbara Villiers, Mrs Palmer, afterwards Lady Castlemaine and duchess of Cleveland, who did her best to ruin him. To her king Charles handed over the revenues of the Post Office and the Customs, and he gave her the rents of Phoenix Park in Dublin and wide estates in Surrey. She shared his promiscuous affections with Louise de Kéroualle, duchess of Portsmouth (an agent of King Louis XIV), Frances Stuart, duchess of Richmond (so beautiful that she was the model for Britannia on the reverse of the coinage), and Hortensia Mancini, duchess of Mazarin (a niece of the Cardinal), besides the actresses Nell Gwynne, Moll Davis and Margaret Hughes, amongst others. Altogether Charles II left fifteen illegitimate children (six dukes among them), as well as some who died in infancy.

In 1661 Charles married the Portuguese Princess Catherine of Braganza, who brought him a dowry of £500,000, besides Tangier and Bombay. The marriage was childless, but Queen Catherine was always treated with great respect by the king and by the Court (although the duchess of Cleveland was appointed to be one of the ladies of her bedchamber). Because of her childlessness the Roman Catholic James, Duke of York, was left heir to the throne, and there were repeated rumours of a divorce. Buckingham and Shaftesbury are said to have pressed the king to acknowledge a marriage to Lucy Walter, but Charles would have none of it, and thrice denied to the Privy Council any previous marriage.

II

On the evening of Sunday, 1st February 1685, the day before the king was taken ill with his last, fatal illness, John Evelyn, the diarist, was in the palace at Whitehall, and left a vivid description of the scene. Evelyn is described briefly in the *Dictionary of National Biography* as 'virtuoso'; he was a wealthy country gentleman who took no part in politics and lived quietly in the country and abroad during the Civil War and through the Commonwealth. He was one of the founders of the Royal Society, and his famous diary, which covered the years 1640 to 1706, remained in manuscript and was not published until 1818, when it was edited by the antiquary, William Bray.

'I can never forget,' wrote Evelyn, 'the inexpressible luxury and prophanenesse, gaming and all dissolutenesse, and as it were total forgetfullnesse of God (it being Sunday evening) which this day se'nnight I was witness of, the King sitting and toying with his concubines, Portsmouth, Cleveland, and Mazarine; a French boy singing love songs, in that glorious gallery, whilst about 20 of the greate courtiers and other dissolute persons were at Basset round a large table, a bank of at least 2000 in gold before them, upon which two gentlemen who were with me made reflexions with astonishment. Six days after was all in the dust!'

When King Charles rose from his bed on the Monday morning his attendants and the noblemen who as usual were present noticed that he was unusually pale and that his speech was indistinct when he made an effort to converse. As he was being shaved he had what was described as an 'apoplectic fit', cried out and fell into the arms of Lord Ailesbury, his Gentleman of the Bedchamber. By chance Dr Edmund King (M.D., F.R.S., knighted in 1686), who had charge of the royal crucibles and retorts, was in the room and with his lancet withdrew at once sixteen ounces of blood from a vein in the king's left arm. This apparently gave immediate relief, but he continued to have convulsions and fainting attacks.

All the Court physicians were summoned (one prescription is signed by fourteen of them), regardless of politics or creed – it was a matter of comment that among them were Whigs and Roman Catholics – and they ordered three cupping-glasses to be applied to his shoulders and deep scarification to be carried out, which removed another eight ounces of blood. A few moments later, 'to free his stomach of all impurities', a strong antimonial emetic was given, but as the king could swallow only a small portion of this, it was followed by a large dose of zinc sulphate in paeony water.

Strong purgatives were then administered – 'two-blend pills', the chief ingredients being colocynth, scammony and oil of cloves – accelerated by a succession of enemas or 'clysters' made, first, from a decoction of herbs, violet and camomile leaves and linseed, and then from more potent ingredients, antimonial wine and rock salt. His head was shaved and, 'so as to leave no stone unturned', pungent blistering agents were applied all over his head, followed by the red-hot cautery. Strange to say – at least, according to our modern ideas – the royal patient reacted favourably to this drastic treatment and in two hours consciousness was completely restored, so that he was able to give his own account of his symptoms.

III

When it was realized that the king was seriously ill, the antechambers and galleries at Whitehall were soon full to overflowing, and the sickroom itself was filled with peers, privy councillors and foreign ambassadors. There are in fact few episodes in history better documented than the deathbed of King Charles II, for eight different accounts of it exist which were written by persons who were actually in the room with him, including official reports by the ambassadors of France and Holland to their respective Courts.

These first-hand accounts include the *Memoirs* of Thomas, second Lord Ailesbury, who was with the king both before and during his illness, sharing his bedroom at night; also the diary and letters of Philip, second earl of Chesterfield, who likewise was by the side of the king. The tract published by the Benedictine monk, John Hudleston, who at the end administered extreme unction to the king, gives 'A brief account of what occurred on his [i.e. the King's] deathbed in regard to religion: London, 1688, quarto'. An anonymous letter to the Rev Francis Roper, Fellow of St John's College, Cambridge, was apparently written on the day following the king's death by one of the chaplains to the bishop of Ely, who stood beside the deathbed. The account in the *Life* of King James II is said to have been compiled from his lost memoirs in his own handwriting. The despatches of Barillon, the French ambassador in London, to King Louis XIV, and the despatches of Van Citters, the Dutch Ambassador, both still exist – or did at least in 1909. Most important of all, however, is the manuscript account of the king's death, with details of the prescriptions of his physicians, by Sir Charles Scarburgh, M.D., which is in the library of the Society of Antiquaries at Burlington House.

A contemporary broadsheet in the Somers Collection at the British Museum reads as follows: '*A True Relation of the Late King's Death*. On Monday, being the 2nd of February, the King rose early, saying that he had not slept well the last Night: And about seven of the Clock, coming from his private Devotions, out of his Closet, fell down (and scarce any sign of Life remaining in him for the space of four Houres) of a Fit of an Apoplexy, but with the loss of sixteen Ounces of Blood, and other Applications, came again to his Senses, and great Hopes were of his Recovery, till Thursday one of the Clock; so that at five, the Doctors being come before the Council, declared that the K . . . was in great Danger; and on Friday, a quarter before twelve, he departed this Life. God have Mercy on his Soul.'

The term 'apoplexy' had at that time a much wider meaning than today, when it is held to mean a haemorrhage into the brain due to the rupture of an artery, usually in a person (a male much more commonly than a female) with a high blood pressure or a small intra-cranial aneurysm. But in the seventeenth century and even considerably later 'apoplexy' included all sorts of sudden seizures, with or without loss of consciousness – epilepsy, hysteria, infantile convulsions, even coma from diabetes or kidney disease.

The word 'fit' had a similarly vague connotation, and was used to mean not only epilepsy but a rigor, such as in ague (as malaria in England was for long described), septicaemia or other high fevers. The 'fits' which King Charles II is said to have had previously were in all probability ague.

IV

On the evening of Monday, the first day of the king's illness, his physicians again met in consultation and pronounced him out of immediate danger. But with a view to 'diverting and withdrawing the humours from his head, and at the same time to give strength to his loaded brain', they prescribed 'the sacred bitter powder', hierapicra, a compound of cinnamon, zedoaria, avarum, cardamom seeds, saffron, cochineal, and aloes, along with bryony compound, reputed to be an emetic, purgative, and diuretic. In addition, a powder of white hellebore root was administered, to excite sneezing, and a powder of cowslip flowers 'to strengthen the brain'.

Then, for the night, manna with cream of tartar in barley water, was prescribed as a laxative; and, to counteract the scalding of the urine likely to arise from the use of blistering drugs (such as cantharides) an emulsion of decoction of barley with liquorice, and sweet almond kernels, sweetened with white sugar, was prescribed, to be taken as often as required. Nourishment was ordered in the form of light broth and of ale made without hops, to be taken alternately with the emulsion.

Spirit of sal ammoniac was applied from time to time to the king's nostrils 'both as a cerebral stimulant and to excite sneezing'; and, in addition, 'to promote still further both the revulsion and the derivation from his head', cephalic plasters (an ingredient of which was pigeon's dung), combined with equal parts of spurge and burgundy pitch, were applied to the soles of his feet.

Next morning, Tuesday, another consultation was held, at which twelve physicians were present, and congratulated themselves on the success of the remedies they had prescribed, resolving therefore to continue on the same lines. The king complained of a pain in his throat, and a superficial excoriation was found, probably due to the efforts to separate his teeth during a convulsion; for this an astringent and soothing gargle was prescribed.

To guard against a recurrence of convulsions an antispasmodic 'julep' was prescribed, consisting of black cherry water, flowers of lime, lilies of the valley, paeony compound, compound spirit of lavender, 'prepared pearls', and white candy sugar to taste. A further ten ounces of blood were drawn from the jugular veins, and 'as the need for purgation was still urgent', a laxative mixture was given as well.

On Wednesday afternoon, not surprisingly, the patient had a relapse, with renewed convulsions, and a small draught of 'spirit of human skull' was administered – 'a sure harbinger', as Sir Raymond Crawfurd wrote, 'of impending dissolution'. This decoction, which was prepared from the skull of a person who had died a violent death, was employed in convulsive disorders, no doubt to excite horror and so act by suggestion.

The king's physicians were pressed by his ministers for an opinion on his illness, but they refused to say anything definite and were obviously worried as well as puzzled. However, some sort of intermittent fever was at the time prevalent in London, and on Thursday morning the physicians decided to give their patient Peruvian bark febrifuge (i.e. crude quinine powder). The prescription was signed by the following fourteen physicians: T. Witherly, T. Millington, T. Short, Edm. King, E. Farrell, C. Scarburgh, Edm. Dickenson, E. Browne, C. Frasier, M. Lister, Wr. Charleton, R. Lower, F. Mendes, and F. Lefebre.

They were now optimistic enough to report to the Privy Council: 'That they conceive His Majesty to be in a condition of safety, and that he will in a few days be freed from his distemper.' It was on this

Thursday that King Charles made his famous remark to the friends around him: 'He had been,' he said, 'a most unconscionable time dying, but he hoped that they would excuse it.'

That evening the king's brother, James, duke of York, observing that King Charles had refused the sacrament from Dr Ken, the bishop of Bath and Wells, asked if he might send for a priest. The king answered, 'For God's sake do, brother, and lose no time'. But of the priests who were in the palace those of Queen Catherine were Portuguese and those of the duchess of York Italian, none of them speaking English.

By chance there was in Whitehall at the time John Hudleston, a Benedictine monk who, at great risk to himself, had saved the king's life after the battle of Worcester, and on that account had been, ever since the Restoration, a privileged person. Disguised in a wig and gown, Hudleston was smuggled into the king's apartment, and the attendant crowd, except for the duke of York and the king's intimate friends, the earl of Bath and the earl of Feversham, were removed on some excuse. Hudleston knelt by the king's bed, listened to his confession, pronounced the absolution, and administered extreme unction.

King Charles handed his keys to his brother, saying that he had left all his possessions to him, and asked him to be kind to the duchesses of Cleveland and Portsmouth, 'and that Nelly might not starve'.

On Friday morning the king was seized with breathlessness, he was again bled, and desperate heart remedies were administered, including 'Raleigh's stronger antidote' (an extract of different parts of an enormous number of herbs and animals), Goa stone, and Oriental Bezoar stone. The 'true Bezoar' was a concretion formed in the stomach of an East Indian goat, believed to have magical power in destroying poisons and re-animating the vital powers. The 'false Bezoar' or 'Goa stones' were powdered oyster shells made into small balls, perfumed with ambergris.

At half-past eight in the morning the king's speech began to fail, at ten o'clock he was unconscious, and shortly before noon he passed quietly away at the age of 54.

V

A post-mortem examination took place on the next day, and the report by Sir Charles Scarburgh, first physician to the king, reads as follows: 'In the body of Charles the Second, Most August King of the Britains, when opened after death were found: 1. On the Surface of the Brain the Veins and Arteries were unduly full. 2. All the Cerebral ventricles were filled with a kind of serous matter, and the substance of the Brain itself was quite soaked with similar fluid. 3. On the right side the Lungs and Pleura were firmly adherent to the chest-wall, but on the left side they were quite free, as Nature has ordained they should be in health. 4. No fault whatever could be found with the substance of the Lungs, but they were charged with blood. 5. The heart was large and firm, and quite free from malformation in every part. 6. In the depths of the belly there was nothing unnatural, except that the Liver was inclined to be livid in colour, perhaps because of the abundance of blood in it, with which the kidneys and spleen were also engorged.'

Sir Charles Scarburgh wrote his detailed account of the last illness and death of King Charles II in Latin, giving all the prescriptions in full, with the signatures of the various physicians. Educated at St Paul's School and Caius College, Cambridge, he became a Fellow of the College and taught mathematics. He lost his Fellowship and his library under the Commonwealth, then went to Merton College, Oxford, studied medicine and took his M.D. in 1646. He was a friend of Pepys, became a Fellow of the College of Physicians in 1648, was knighted in 1669, and died in 1694.

Sir Raymond Crawfurd, classical scholar and physician to King's College Hospital, who translated and edited Scarburgh's manuscript, suggests that the most probable cause of the death of King Charles II was Bright's disease, or inflammation of the kidneys, followed by uraemia (with convulsions) and coma. All his life

Charles had lived hard, in his youth he had endured privations, he ate and drank to excess, and latterly attacks of gout had prevented exercise. At the time of his sudden and unexpected death there were many rumours that the king had been poisoned, a suggestion that Crawfurd, in company with Hume, Macaulay and other historians, dismisses with brief contempt. But the available evidence makes this suggestion at least worthy of examination.

The fourteen physicians around his sickbed contradicted each other. Some thought that the 'fit' was epileptic and that he should 'have his doze out'; others that it was apoplectic, demanding bleeding, purging, and vomiting. Eventually the majority decided that it was a fever, and 'bark' (i.e. crude quinine) administered.

One of the physicians, Dr. Thomas Short, a Roman Catholic and a man of great learning and integrity, declared to some of his intimate friends that he believed that there had been foul play at the death of King Charles II. Later on, Dr James Welwood, physician to Queen Mary, wife of King William III, gave a number of arguments in favour of the suggestion that King Charles was poisoned. It has been emphasized that the post-mortem examination showed no evidence of poisoning; but the examination was directed chiefly to the brain, and the oesophagus, stomach and intestines were never examined at all, in spite of the abdominal pains of which the stricken king had complained. And when one of the physicians present seemed to be unusually inquisitive about the condition of the stomach and bowels, he was reproved for his 'needless curiosity'.

There is no doubt that the death of Charles II came very opportunely for James, duke of York, and his supporters. If he had lived for only a few weeks longer the Protestant duke of Monmouth might have been recalled to Court, the duke of York sent (as had been done before) to Scotland or abroad, the unpopular Ministers dismissed, and a new parliament summoned.

The night before the illness began, when the king was in bed he was overheard to groan during most of the night, he complained of 'a heavy oppression' in his stomach and over his heart, and afterwards of a sharp abdominal pain. In the morning he was pale and had a 'ghastly' look, and when he sat down to be shaved, just before the first 'fit' came on, he could not sit straight, but sat in a stooping posture, with his hand on his stomach. After he had been relieved by bleeding he complained of a 'racking pain' in his stomach and of no other symptoms. And during the whole illness in bed he was observed to hold his hand for the most part upon his stomach, moaning with pain.

It is true that King Charles apparently had no suspicion of poisoning and made no mention of it, but he could hardly speak. And it is also true that at that time it was not unusual for the general public to attribute an unexpected death in the case of an important personage to poisoning—King James I, for instance, had been accused of poisoning his heir, Prince Henry (who died of typhoid fever), and even King Charles I of poisoning King James I.

Nevertheless, there were in the case of King Charles II a number of circumstances that might well make one suspect poisoning, and the verdict nearly three hundred years later cannot be more certain than 'not proven'.

REFERENCES

The Life and Writings of John Evelyn, Esq., F.R.S., 2 vols., edited by William Bray. Colburn, London 1818.

DAVID HUME. History of England, 8 vols. Cadell, etc., London 1818.

W. D. FELLOWES. Historical Sketches of Charles the First, Cromwell, Charles the Second, etc., John Murray, London 1828.

J. FITZGERALD MOLLOY. Royalty Restored: London under Charles II, Ward and Downey, London 1885.

J. J. JUSSERAND. A French Ambassador at the Court of Charles the Second, Fisher Unwin, London 1892.

MONSIGNOR A. S. BARNES. Downside Review, July, 1900.

RAYMOND CRAWFURD. *The Last Days of Charles II*, Clarendon Press Oxford 1909.

C. L. TAYLOR. *Some Royal Death-Beds: Charles II*. British Medical Journal, 25th June, 1910, Vol. *i*, p. 1557.

LORD MACAULAY. *History of England*, edited by C. H. Firth, 6 vols. Macmillan, London 1913.

The Diary of John Evelyn, edited by E. S. de Beer, 6 vols. Clarendon Press, Oxford 1955.